FIVE ROADS TO THE PACIFIC

To

my sons

Philip and Richard

Five Roads to the Pacific

by

NETA LOHNES FRAZIER

j 9795

DAVID McKAY COMPANY, INC.

New York

1964

ACKNOWLEDGMENTS:

My grateful thanks to Mrs. Elizabeth Gilbert, Assistant Librarian of
the Spokane Public Library, her colleague, Miss Mary Johnson of the
reference department, Mrs. Betty W. Bender, Librarian of the Eastern Washington Historical Society's library in the Cowles Memorial
Museum and Mrs. Margaret Magelssen for their valuable assistance
in helping me find the material for this book.

My special thanks to Miss Dorothy Elliott of Walla Walla, for free
use of her valuable collection of historical material, wherein I found
the idea for this book.

My gratitude also to my companions in adventure, Mrs. Gladys S.
Puckett, Mrs. Gertrude E. Finney and Mrs. Marian Quackenbush,
with whom I visited some of the historical sites herein mentioned,
in the summer of 1963.

Finally, my sincere thanks to my daughter, Mrs. Lesley Thompson,
and the members of the Spokane Penwomen, for critical assistance
with the manuscript.

N.L.F.

CONTENTS

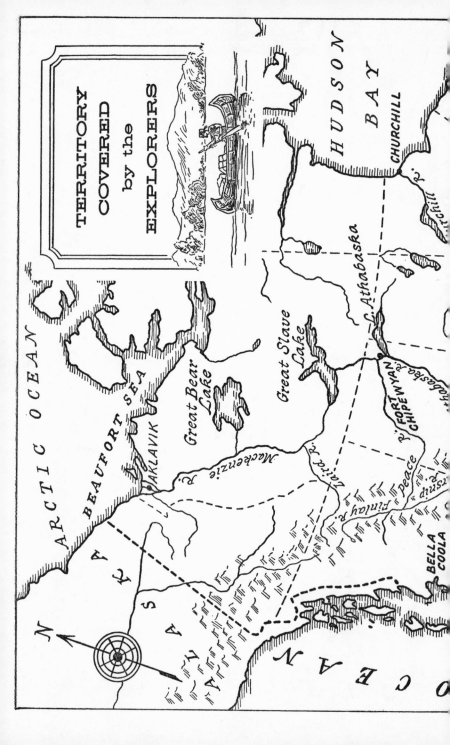

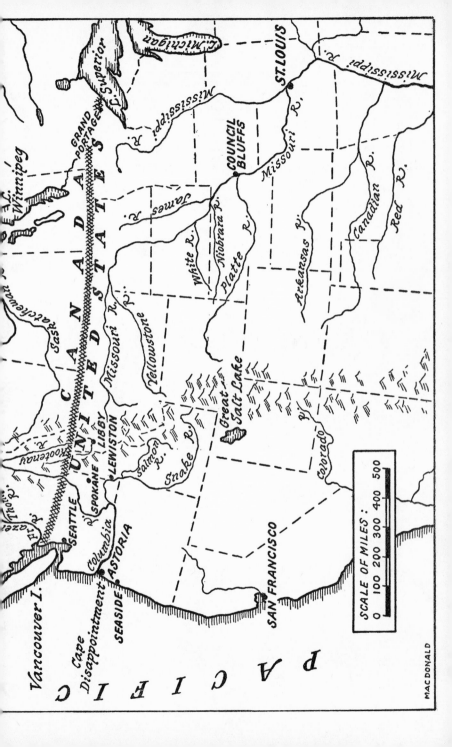

Westward Ho! 19—

IT IS 5:45 P.M., Eastern Daylight Time, at Kennedy Airport on Long Island. Over the loudspeaker comes the announcement: "Northwest Airlines Jet Flight 33, non-stop to Seattle-Tacoma, now boarding at Gate Four."

Joe and Bill show their tickets and mount the steps into the great plane.

"You sit by the window, Bill, since it's your first flight."

"Don't know if I want to. I feel kinda funny."

"Relax. Nothing to it."

The doors are closed. Smoothly the plane rolls down the runway and takes to the air.

"Joe, is that really the Atlantic Ocean down under us?"

"Sure thing. We're circling around to start West. Look at those poor guys down there on the freeway, driving home to dinner. Bumper to bumper."

"Know something? Right now, I'd trade places."

"Forget it, Bill. Here come the stewardesses with the dinner trays. Takes quite a while to serve a hundred people. Looks as if they're starting at the other end of the plane, too."

"That's fine with me. What are you doing to your watch?"

"Setting it back three hours to Pacific Time, so it will be right when we land."

"Are we moving? Seems to me we're standing still up here in the sky."

"We're moving, all right. Look down there. The Allegheny Mountains."

"So soon?"

"Our trays at last. See that smudge off there? That's Chicago."

"All this time just to get to Chicago?"

"You're catching on, Bill."

"What are those white spots down there below us?"

"Snow. On the peaks of the Rockies."

"Is that water down there the Pacific Ocean?"

"Next thing to it—Puget Sound. And here we are, right on time."

Bill grins. "Nothing to it."

The doors are opened. Bill and Joe walk down the steps and into the concourse. Bill stops beside a window. "Look at those poor guys out there on the freeway. Bumper to bumper. Where do you suppose they are going?"

"Home to dinner, boy."

Bill wrinkles his forehead. "We cross the continent while men in cars are driving home to dinner. I wonder—"

"What, Bill?"

"How did the first guys come across? Cars? No, it must have been before cars. Trains?"

"Before that, I guess. Wagons, perhaps. Or horseback. Maybe even on foot."

"I wonder how long it took guys on foot."

"I think I can tell you," says another passenger standing near them. "I couldn't help overhearing you. It took the first explorer, Alexander Mackenzie, thirteen years to reach the Pacific Ocean; the others, not quite so long."

"Thirteen years!" Joe exclaims.

"How many succeeded?" asks Bill.

"Five expeditions. By five different roads. If you want to know more about it—"

"We certainly do. Flying across, looking down on all those plains and rivers and mountains, has made us curious," says Joe. "Where can we find out about those five expeditions?"

"I've written a book."

"We'll read it."

This is the book.

THE FIRST ROAD

Alexander Mackenzie, 1793

I

MONTREAL was cold and gray with fog that September morning in 1780. Mist lay heavy over the St. Lawrence and dripped from the spars of the ship moored close to the warehouse of Gregory, McLeod and Company, Fur Traders. Already, down in her hold, the sailors were at work by lantern light, bringing up boxes and bales of goods. Shouts and the rattle of chains penetrated the thin walls of the building to the office in the front corner. There, the youngest of the clerks, Alexander Mackenzie, who had been up half the night completing the tally of yesterday's unloading, still lay asleep on a pile of furs.

Continued pounding on the great doors at the side of the warehouse roused him. He sprang from his rough bed and raced through to open them. As the men poured in with their barrow loads, he rushed around lighting lanterns and pointing out where the bales and bundles were to be placed.

Then back to the office, to kindle a fire in the fireplace and swing a kettle of water on the crane for the partners' morning tea. The account books must be laid out, fresh pens cut from goose quills and ink powder mixed with water in the ink horns, before he dared stop to cook his own meager breakfast of oatmeal porridge.

Somehow, he accomplished everything and had washed his saucepan and hung it on its peg when Mr. Gregory and Mr. McLeod rumbled in. They stood close to the warm fire and smacked their lips over the fragrant tea. Alexander snatched up his tally book and hurried out to the warehouse, a tall, sturdy lad of seventeen with thick brown hair, steady hazel eyes and a ruddy complexion. As he left the office, the partners nodded to each other. This boy would do.

Alexander did not see their look. Already he was deep in his work. This was one of the busier times of the year. The fur brigades were coming in from the upper country with their loads of pelts to be recorded, graded and sorted for shipment to London. Not only that, but the ship which was to carry them had only just arrived, having been delayed in her westward passage by heavy storms. It was this which had kept him up so late the night before. The cargo being unloaded must be checked and stored and the ship reloaded as quickly as possible so she could reach England before the winter gales began. Everything was to be done at once.

Alexander had been a clerk for a year and had four more to go. Born in Scotland, he had lost his mother at eleven, whereupon his father, Kenneth Mackenzie, had brought the boy to the home of his brother-in-law, John Maciver, a merchant in New York City. When the Revolutionary War broke out, both men had entered the Loyalist forces, sending the boy to a schoolmaster in Montreal to continue his education.

Alexander would never forget the day word came of the death of both father and uncle. He was alone in the world except for another uncle and some cousins in Scotland who probably had forgotten him. He could not expect the schoolmaster to keep him now that no more money would come from his father.

"I'm sorry, lad," the old man had said.

Alexander had lifted his sea chest to his strong young shoulder. "I'll find work wi' the fur traders. Some day I'll be an explorer like the men of whom you have taught me—Henry Hudson, Frobisher, Foxe—you'll see."

"And be proud to say that Alexander Mackenzie, the great explorer, was my pupil."

After the first year, Alexander had begun to chafe at the confinement of the dark, cold warehouse, with the offensive smell of raw pelts always in his nostrils. He did not want to spend his whole life procuring the makings of high beaver hats and fur cloaks for the royalty and nobles of Europe and China.

Since childhood, he had felt the call of distant places. Here, eight hundred miles inland from the Atlantic Ocean, he was still on the bare edge of the vast country called Canada. What lay out there in the wilderness beyond the fringes of the fur trade? Where did the rivers go? How far was it to the Pacific Ocean? Men had sailed around the globe and up the western shores of this new continent but no one, ever, had crossed it from one ocean to the other.

"That is what I should like to do," he told his fellow clerks.

"Better keep still about it if you ever hope to leave Montreal. Mr. McTavish wants us to spend our time getting furs, not exploring the country."

Alexander, like everyone else in the business, stood in awe of Simon McTavish, the leading agent in Montreal. Shrewd, clever, determined to wrest the last shilling of profit from the business, he was intolerant of anyone who opposed his ideas. Aware of the great expanse of Canada already covered by his traders, he saw no need for further explorations. So if a man in McTavish's employ dreamed of such foolishness, he had best keep his dreams to himself.

Already somewhat aloof by nature it was not too hard for

Alexander to discipline himself to silence, but this did not mean he dropped his ambition. On the contrary, it grew stronger every day and soon an unexpected event even strengthened his determination. From his uncle in Scotland he received a package which contained a new suit of clothes and a small book, *Travels Through the Interior Parts of North-America*, by Jonathan Carver. An accompanying letter read:

> Dear Nephew: Your schoolmaster wrote me of your father's death. I am very sorry. I wish I had the means to bring you back to Scotland but by now you are a grown man and, I doubt not, independent like your father. He had ordered this suit for himself. I hope it will fit you. My eldest boy, Roderick, now thirteen, asks me to tell you he intends to come out to join you in Canada in a few years. As to the book, everyone here is talking about it and the pity that Master Carver died before he could know of its success. I found it good reading.
>
> 　　　　　Y'rs Respectfully,
> 　　　　　James Mackenzie

A warm glow filled Alexander's heart. He was not forgotten. The suit was, in a way, a gift from his dead father. And to think that Roderick remembered him! At that moment began the strong affection for his cousin that was to last all his life.

Most exciting of all, however, was the book. He could hardly wait to finish his day's work and light his candle to begin reading it. A page or two and words leaped out at him:

> The four most capital rivers on the Continent of North-America, viz. the St. Lawrence, the Mississippi, the River Bourbon and the Oregon, or River of the

West, have their sources in the same neighborhood. . . . This shows that these parts are the highest in North-America. . . . In their passage from this spot to the Bay of St. Lawrence, east; to the Bay of Mexico, south; to Hudson's Bay, north; and to the bay at the Straits of Anian, west, each of them traverses upwards of two thousand miles.

The candle flickered and went out but Alexander did not notice. He lay on his back, absorbed in the vision pictured by Carver. He fancied himself floating somewhere high in the heavens, looking down on the continent of North America. There it lay, stretched from the Atlantic to the Pacific, but drawn up in the middle as one might draw a pile of clay to a peak. Down the four sides, from a common source, flowed the four great rivers.

The St. Lawrence he knew personally and he had heard of the Mississippi. The other two were new to him. Perhaps "Bourbon" was an earlier name for the Nelson, that emptied into Hudson's Bay. The one that most intrigued him was the Oregon, River of the West. Where was it? Had anyone ever seen it? Carver said it flowed into the Straits of Anian. Alexander remembered that his school books had mentioned this strait as the western end of the supposed Northwest Passage, the water link between the two great oceans for which explorers had searched from the time of Columbus. Many people doubted its existence but here was Carver speaking of it as a fact.

Could he be right? Was it, perhaps, not an open strait but a passage by means of lakes and rivers already known and then by this great Unknown, the River of the West? Too bad Carver had not been permitted to find it himself. Someone else would have to do it.

Alexander felt as if a hand touched his shoulder. A voice seemed to speak in his ear, "Why not you?"

Shaking, he sat up in bed. Who had spoken? Was it the voice of God? Was this to be his mission in life? By the time he had finished the book, he knew it was.

The new clothes he packed away in his sea chest. They were meant for strolling idly on Sundays to catch the eye of a pretty girl. No time for that now. He had work to do. He told no one of his determination. In no way must he antagonize Simon McTavish since only by means of the fur trade could he ever hope to get to the far West. He worked harder than ever and the more he learned about the business, the more interested he became.

Since the fur trade was the basis not only for Mackenzie's explorations but also for those of the other great expeditions, it is well for us, also, to understand how it was organized and conducted.

For centuries, furs had been the visual sign of wealth and importance. What so beautiful as rich fur trimmings for silk and velvet tunics and gowns? What so comfortable as a fur-lined cloak to wrap about the shivering royal person when bitter winds whipped through the drafty, unheated old family castle?

The forests of Germany, Finland and Russia abounded in fur-bearing animals, most popular of which was the beaver. For a long time this source was sufficient for the needs of Europe, but about the year 1510, hatters learned how to beat sheared beaver fur into luxurious thick fabric for making high-crowned, broad-brimmed headgear. Here was a fabulous new way to demonstrate prestige—the higher the hat crown, the nobler the head beneath it. ("Don't high-hat me," growled the king to his courtiers, who were forbidden to wear a hat taller than the royal covering.)

With this new outlet for furs, supplies soon began to run short.

How fortunate, then, that explorers searching for the Northwest Passage through the newly discovered continent of North America, found instead a seemingly inexhaustible source of beaver, fox, marten and other animals whose fur could be bought from Indian trappers for a few pennies' worth of bright calico, a shiny button or an inch of tobacco twist.

By Mackenzie's time, the Hudson's Bay Company, oldest and largest of the fur-trading concerns, had existed for well over one hundred years. Its plan had always been to have the Indians bring their furs directly to its trading posts or "factories" on the Bay and there take in exchange the goods provided by the company. In time, the beaver, the principal fur-bearing animal of the trade, was cleaned out in the great "muskrat country" around the Bay and the Indians were forced to range farther and farther for their furs. Often they spent nearly half the year traveling to and from Hudson's Bay.

This situation opened the way for competing companies centered in Montreal. By 1780 there were several who sent traders with goods out to where the Indians lived so they did not have to make the long journeys eastward. The red men were not slow to take advantage of the change. The new companies flourished, though now it was the white man who must make the long journeys and carry the loads of trade goods.

The individual who made this possible was the lowly French-Canadian voyageur or canoeman. An American, Thomas L. Mc-Kenney, who visited Canada in 1826, described him thus:

> They are short, thick set, and active, and never tire. A Canadian, if born to be a labourer, deems himself to be very unfortunate if he should chance to grow over five feet five or six inches—and if he shall reach five feet ten or eleven, it forever excludes him from the privilege of

becoming a voyageur. There is no room for the legs of such people in these canoes. But if he shall stop growing at about five feet four inches, and be gifted with a good voice and lungs that never tire, he is considered as having been born under a most favourable star.

These men paddled at forty strokes to the minute and in good water could raise it to sixty. They kept time by chanting endless verses of old French songs, hence the need for a good voice, and could paddle eighteen hours a day with only a few stops. On the frequent portages they were each expected to carry at least two "pieces," as the standard ninety-pound packs were called, at one time. These were placed in a sling hung from a carrying band around the man's forehead and rested on his back. Bent nearly double under the load, he dog-trotted rather than walked across the portage. Often he must make two trips and help carry the canoe besides.

In the East, the canoemen were called "pork eaters," the word in French being *mangeurs de lard,* which suggests the nature of their pork. In the West, they lived on pemmican, an Indian food made of dried buffalo meat or venison, pounded fine and mixed with an equal amount of melted fat. When hard, it kept for a long time and was very nourishing but no one ever said it tasted good.

Though naturally cheerful, even gay, the voyageur was emotional, superstitious and easily frightened by any unusual sight, weather condition, or story. He could neither read nor write nor did he miss these skills in the wilderness. He was childishly vain, fond of bright colors and fancy clothes. Plumes, ribbons, banners, a bright handkerchief around his head—all these were his delight. His was a bitter, gruelling life and he was usually worn out by the age of forty. Why did he choose it? The answer was freedom.

His kind, in Europe, must kowtow to the lord of the manor. Here in Canada, in the wilderness, he was his own man.

And what was in the packs carried to the Indian with such effort after it had been shipped over from England in sailing ships? First of all, guns and ammunition. A gun made an Indian the master of his enemies and the wild animals that were his food. Next, he wanted woolen and cotton cloth, blankets, thread, lines and twine, knives, awls and heavy needles, kettles of brass, copper and sheet iron, silk and cotton handkerchiefs, bright coats and hats and always tobacco. This item was put out in long twists and sold by the inch.

For these much-desired goods, the Indian, in turn, traded in the average year over two hundred thousand beaver pelts, sixty thousand marten, thirty thousand muskrat and lesser numbers of bear, fox, otter, mink, lynx, wolverine, fisher, raccoon, wolf, elk, deer and buffalo skins.

The standard unit was the beaver and prices may be indicated by the fact that one blanket cost seven or eight skins; one fathom (six feet) of twist tobacco, four, and an axe, three pelts.

The Montreallers, as the smaller companies were called, were run by the financial agents in Montreal. Under them came the partners who manned the trading posts and below them, the clerks. Everyone in the company had to work up from this beginning by serving an apprenticeship of five to seven years, the total salary being one hundred pounds. After that, if they made good, they might become partners themselves and share in the profits.

These profits, Alexander learned, could with luck be enormous, up to one thousand per cent every second year. Yet there were many hazards and only a few men actually became wealthy. He hoped he might be one of these, not for the sake of money itself, but to enable him to carry out his dreams of exploration.

At the end of his apprenticeship, having pleased the agents and kept his ambitions to himself, he was chosen to take a venture of goods to Detroit, some eight hundred miles farther inland, to prove whether or not he was worthy to become a partner. His cousin, Roderick Mackenzie, who had come from Scotland as he planned, took his place as clerk.

The next phase of the business that Alexander had to learn was the means and routes of transportation. A glimpse at the map of Canada reveals its great network of lakes and rivers. For this kind of country the horse was of no use. Travel must be mostly by water. The birchbark canoe was the ideal craft. Made of the bark of yellow birch, applied to a framework of tough white cedar with melted pine gum, it was light and easy to handle. In the bottom were laid long slats or poles on which to place the load. Narrow boards, not more than four inches wide, were fastened just below the outer rim or gunwale as seats for the paddlemen.

On the eastern run, from Montreal to Grand Portage on Lake Superior, large canoes were used, thirty-five to forty feet in length, carrying a ton and a half of merchandise and manned by eight or ten men. They sat two abreast, using short paddles. At the ends, which curved up to a high prow and stern, sat the bowman and steersman, wielding longer paddles.

The most popular route from Montreal was by way of the Ottawa River and Lake Nipissing to Georgian Bay and Lake Huron, thence along the north shore to the Falls of St. Mary, now called Sault Ste. Marie, into Lake Superior. From this point the canoes hugged the safer north shore almost five hundred miles to Grand Portage, near the western end.

Mackenzie, who left a careful, detailed account of this route in his book, *Voyages,* told of thirty-six carrying places or portages in this distance. At each one the canoe must be entirely unloaded and contents and canoe carried to the next water. He calculated the entire trip as about fifteen hundred miles of which seventy-five to a hundred were in the "carries." The distance in these was counted in "paces," a measure of about two and one-half feet. They varied in number from twenty-five to as many as fifteen hundred in a single portage.

An alternate route was down the St. Lawrence in canoes to Kingston at the entrance of Lake Ontario. Here the goods were transferred to sailing ships of fifty to seventy tons for the lake run to Niagara. An overland portage of ten miles around the great falls led to the river above where again canoes were used as far as Lake Erie. Here another ship took the goods through the lake and up the Detroit River to the post of that name. To go on from this point, another large ship transported them up the Lake and River St. Clair and coasted the western shore of Lake Huron to Michilimackinac, at the junction of Lakes Huron and Michigan, where the company maintained a large and important post. Canoes again took up the journey as far as Sault Ste. Marie and still another ship finished the haul to Grand Portage.

This route, Mackenzie wrote, was less expensive than the other but more dangerous and took so much more time that goods did not reach Grand Portage in time for the summer visits of the western traders.

Grand Portage, about midway across the continent, was the great hub of the trade, where the inland traders came to exchange the year's collection of pelts for the next season's supply of goods. From the farthest western posts men must journey fifteen hundred to two thousand miles, often requiring two months of steady travel. Grand Portage was, therefore, the most distant place they could reach in the short summer season and get back before ice closed the rivers.

Mackenzie's first trip began on a bright May morning in 1785, with the company flag at the prow of the leading canoe and rib-

bons and banners flying in the breeze. The men, in new clothes
that were part of their wages, kept time for their paddles with a
favorite song:

> *Ma-l-brouck has gone a-fighting,*
> *Mironton, mironton, mirontaine—*

that continued
through many verses recounting the exploits of Lord Marl-
borough.

Up the river they paddled to the end of the Island of Montreal
to make confession and receive a final blessing at St. Ann's, the
last church they would see for many months. Here Alexander
and his brigade took the St. Lawrence route for Detroit. He
composed his stern, handsome features so no one would guess the
pounding of his heart as the little flotilla lost sight of the church
and was alone on the great river. He was now the master, with
full responsibility for the lives of his men and the investment in
trade goods given him to handle. He was twenty-two years old
and on his way.

2

MACKENZIE proved so successful in his Detroit venture that two
years later he was made a full partner in a new company formed
by the union of the small Montreal concerns. It was called the
North West Company of Merchants from Canada and its head
and chief agent was Simon McTavish who as yet had no inkling
of the ambitions of his clever young partner, Alexander Mackenzie. To this young man he assigned the task of re-opening a post
on Lake Athabasca, some fifteen hundred miles northwest of
Grand Portage but still three hundred miles east of the Rocky
Mountains. This was the farthest west post of the company up

to this time and most men did not care to serve there. Nothing could have suited Alexander Mackenzie better.

Another partner, Peter Pond, had set up the first post there several years before but in a quarrel he had shot and killed one of his traders. For this he had been brought back to Montreal to stand trial. He had been acquitted but was still in disfavor when Mackenzie was sent to replace him.

"At last things are coming my way," Alexander bragged to Roderick, his cousin, whom he had asked to have transferred to Detroit. "Just you wait. Let me once get that new post started and off I go to find the Oregon and see the Pacific Ocean with my own eyes."

"Hush! Someone may overhear you."

"I'm sick of all this secrecy. I'm a partner now. Why should I have to keep still any longer?"

"So was Peter Pond a partner. But he was like you. He had a dream of some river flowing to the Pacific. Wanted the company to send an exploring party to find it and set up a supply base at the mouth where ships could come from England."

"Where did you hear this?"

"I heard Mr. McTavish discussing it with other partners while I was still in Montreal. It seemed to me not a bad idea. It would save all the long overland haul that takes so many months of each year."

"It's a great idea. Why didn't you tell me about it before? I would have gone to Montreal myself to talk to Mr. McTavish about it."

"I knew you would. That's why I didn't tell you. I didn't want him to ruin you as he has ruined Pond. You don't suppose it was because he killed some crazy-drunk trader that he has been practically thrown out of the company, do you?"

Alexander scowled. "McTavish is growing more narrow-minded each year. Why can't he see the importance of finding that river and opening a trade route to the Pacific? Somebody's going to do it."

"I agree with you, Alex, and I think you are the man. Only don't let McTavish hear of it until you've done it. He is still in control, you remember. From his point of view, the important thing is to get furs. Anything else is disloyalty."

Alexander laughed. "When he hears I've found the Oregon, he will change his mind. I'll open up a fur area to make his mouth water. Come on out there to Athabasca with me and take charge while I go exploring."

Roderick hesitated.

"Only for a year or so," Alexander begged. "Let me once see the Pacific Ocean and I'll be satisfied."

Roderick could never deny his cousin anything. Even though he believed he was courting trouble and might lose his position, he agreed. "For a year or so but no more."

Alexander spun him around in a Highland fling. " 'Twill make you famous, Roddie, lad. Cousin of Alexander Mackenzie, the great explorer."

As soon as they could turn over to their successors in Detroit all the details of that post, the two started for the West. Their first stop, of course, was at Grand Portage where Alexander was to receive his instructions. This was the largest of the Nor'westers' posts, with sometimes as many as twelve hundred canoemen assembled in addition to the usual work force.

It was built like a military fort, surrounded by a palisade eighteen feet high, enclosing a great square. Within stood various offices, storehouses, servants' quarters and lodgings for the clerks. In the center was the large main hall, a log building with a high balcony running around the banquet room. Off the balcony opened the apartments of the partners. The walls were hung with portraits of company officials and here were held great feasts when the partners came together for the annual meetings. The Mackenzies were greatly impressed with the elegance of everything and with the abundance and variety of the food.

Leaving Grand Portage with a crew of voyageurs and half a dozen smaller canoes loaded with supplies, they took the well-defined trade route through Rainy Lake and Lake of the Woods, then by a chain of small lakes, streams and portages to Lake Winnepeg. Here the voyageurs were in their element. Nothing to stop them but wind, storms and high waves. All too soon they came to the mouth of the great Saskatchewan River where again began the toil of tracking or pulling the canoes along by a line and portaging.

The river, muddy with silt, ran in a deep trench it had carved three hundred miles across the bleak, windswept prairie where no trees broke the monotony. The vast emptiness frightened the canoemen and to keep their minds off their fears, Mackenzie drove them unmercifully. The worst portages were called Frog and Methye, leading to the Churchill River where stood Cumberland House, a famous early-day post. Then on by Cumberland Lake and the Clearwater River, three hundred and fifty more difficult miles to Buckingham House and another two hundred to Fort George.

At last they emerged into the great Athabasca River, one of the most beautiful streams of Canada, where pine-wooded hills ran down to the edge of clear water. Here they swung north at the site of the present-day town of McMurray in the Province of Alberta, for the last hundred and fifty mile stretch of water. The ribbons and banners once more came out and the pace quickened.

Thirty miles below the lake they came to Pond's old fort on the river. Here, to Alexander's surprise, he found the veteran Pond himself, sulkily licking his wounds and indulging in his favorite pastime of drawing maps of the West. This was too good an opportunity to miss. Alexander persuaded Roderick to go on ahead and select a place for the new post while he stayed behind to learn what he could.

A little sympathy brought a ready response from the disappointed, bitter Pond. Almost fifty years old, his health impaired by years of hardship and exposure, he knew he could no longer go on exploring trips himself. Willingly he passed on to Mackenzie all his store of information, both true and false, about the country to the north and west.

Three hundred miles farther north, he said, was another and much larger lake than Athabasca. It was called Great Slave Lake and out of it ran a tremendous river, navigable all the way to the Pacific Ocean. This, of course, was not true but neither Pond nor Mackenzie knew it. Alexander's excitement rose to fever pitch.

"In what latitude does it enter the Pacific?" he asked.

"Somewhere above sixty degrees. It flows into Cook's Inlet. Captain James Cook named it for himself but I feel sure it is the same river Jonathan Carver called the Oregon. I have talked with two Indians who said they came up it from the sea. They showed me a blanket they received from a ship trading at the mouth."

"But Cook's Inlet is pretty far north," said Alexander thoughtfully.

"I think Cook may have made a mistake in his observations. Anyhow, the Indians told me this river flows southwest all the way to the ocean."

"Then if we can find it it will complete the water route from Grand Portage to the ocean. The old Northwest Passage, as Carver believed."

"I believe it also," said Pond. "I have tried to convince our partners what a find it would be for our company, but you know McTavish."

"What are you planning to do now, Mr. Pond? You are welcome here so long as I am in charge."

Pond shook his gray head. "I'm a Yankee. I've given the best of my life to the North West Company but now they do not want me any more. I've arranged to sell my share and go back to my old home in Milford, Connecticut, where my children live. I came back here only to get my maps. I intend to place one before the American Congress. If the Nor'westers are not to be first to the Pacific, perhaps the Americans will."

"A Nor'wester will be the man, Mr. Pond, I promise you. All this country must be saved for King George."

As soon as Pond had gone, Alexander paddled down the river to see how Roderick was getting along. His cousin had selected as a site for the new post a long promontory on the south side of the lake, eight miles east of the river outlet. They named it Fort Chipewyan for the nearby Indian tribe. The fishing was good here at all times of the year, an important factor in this distant country where men had to depend almost entirely on fish for food.

After a winter of successful trading, Alexander packed up the furs he had obtained and dispatched them by canoe to Grand Portage. His chance had come. Summer was a time of comparative leisure for fur traders so he felt no compunctions about leaving the post for a few months, especially with Roderick in charge.

To his clerks and canoemen he said only that he was going north to open one or two new trading posts, which actually was part of his plan. For this purpose he took an extra canoe loaded with merchandise and an experienced clerk, M. Laurent Le Roux. They set off on June 3, 1789, banners flying and the cheers of the men in their ears.

Alexander had spent almost nine years in preparation for this moment yet he dared not let anyone except his cousin know what he intended to do. By this time he had learned Indian nature well enough to be sure that if his guides guessed how far they would have to go before they saw home again, they would desert before ever they embarked. In their own surroundings they might be brave and aggressive but detached from family and friends they were as timid as children lost from their mothers.

Mackenzie's second in command was another Scot, Alexander McKay, a very capable man. Had Mackenzie been able to confide in him he would have felt much less lonely, but the habit built up by long years of keeping his thoughts to himself prevented him from sharing them now. His aloofness made him seem cold though his journal reveals his constant anxiety and his sympathy for his shivering, frightened crew.

It consisted of four Canadian boatmen, two of them accompanied by their wives, and one German. The principal guide was an Indian known as the English Chief from the many trips he had made to Hudson's Bay. With him were his two wives, two younger Indian guides and several members of their tribe. They filled three canoes and at that some of the extra baggage, provisions and ammunition had to be added to Mr. Le Roux' load.

Though it was summer by the calendar, ice still floated in the lake and when they entered the Peace River, at the lake's extreme western end, driftwood so choked the channel that canoes could scarcely move. The third day one canoe was smashed to pieces and its contents lost. At once the Indians began to talk about going home. Every morning Mackenzie woke up fearful they had left him during the night, but by giving presents and talking hopefully he kept them going.

Thirty miles up the Peace the flotilla turned into the so-called Slave River which geographers now identify as the Peace itself. It was a noble stream, coiling smoothly through great forests of spruce, white birch, pine, willow, alder and poplar. When a view opened to the west, snow-clad mountains cut a sawtooth skyline. Pelicans, geese and ducks swam leisurely along the shore. Then into Great Slave Lake, three hundred miles long by fifty at its greatest width and covered with ice.

Here was a real setback. The weather was so cold and the rain at times so violent that the brigade would have to stop and unload, taking shelter under the overturned canoes. For two weeks they were forced to camp on shore yet, in spite of the cold, swarms of gnats and mosquitoes covered the men's faces, got into their ears and noses and drove them half wild.

Ice on the lake but, not far back from the shore, the Indian women found quantities of ripe gooseberries and raspberries, a welcome addition to the fish diet. Islands in the lake were dotted with nests of swans, geese and ducks so eggs and meat were plentiful. As the wind veered and the ice moved, channels opened up close to shore. Mackenzie chose a route around the south, east and north sides of the huge lake to take advantage of the protection offered by a chain of islands.

He took frequent observations of the stars but began to regret his lack of astronomical knowledge. All one night he sat up to observe the setting and rising of the sun and made a note that it was below the horizon only four hours and twenty-two minutes. In this brief time open water froze a skin of ice half an inch thick.

At one point on the lake shore they met a tribe of Red-Knife, or as some called them, Yellow-Knife, Indians, the name coming from the copper knives they carried. Le Roux, who understood their dialect, traded for eight packs of good beaver and marten skins and Mackenzie promised to build a trading post here the next year. That should mollify McTavish!

Twenty days after they entered the enormous lake they came

to its outlet. Here, Mackenzie believed, was the beginning of the Great River of the West which he had so long been seeking. He had no way of knowing that almost fifteen hundred miles of exhausting travel lay ahead before he came to its mouth and then it would not be at the Pacific Ocean. Serene in his belief in Pond's story, he set his canoe into the swift current and jingled in his pocket the coins he had brought along to buy goods of the Russians who were known to have trading places on the North Pacific.

Among other things, Pond had told him that this stream ran almost due southwest and had the largest falls in the known world. Alexander kept waiting to reach these falls. Sometimes he fancied he heard their roar and always he was fearful of what might happen to his canoes when they reached them. Would there be sufficient warning to take them out of the water?

For three hundred miles the river flowed west as he had expected, then, surprisingly, swung north. From this point on, the journey was increasingly one of disappointment to Mackenzie. From day to day his observations showed that he was steadily moving northward and the gradual change in the forest from tall, thick willows and birches to short, stunted ones, indicated the same. Indians they met looked upon them with pity and said it would take several winters to reach the sea. Old age would come upon them before they returned. They warned, also, of terrible monsters and impassable falls ahead.

Mackenzie was skeptical of Indian stories but his guides, already tired of the voyage so far from their homes, grew more and more apprehensive and constantly urged him to turn back. One guide became so reluctant that Mackenzie detailed McKay to keep watch of him day and night to prevent his escape. During a thunder storm the guide succeeded in getting away. Mackenzie was very angry at McKay but all he could do was try to find another guide among the tribes they visited. He finally carried one off bodily.

The swift current kept the canoes bouncing along with great speed and high water so covered the rapids that the boatmen found no difficulty in running them. Best of all, no great falls appeared. Mackenzie's observations showed they had crossed the Arctic Circle and they began to see Indians using Eskimo-style bows. They said the ocean was only ten sleeps away.

On July 10, thirty-eight days after they had left Fort Chipewyan, the canoes entered the great spreading delta of the river now known as the Mackenzie. The stream widened to seventy miles and for one hundred miles from its mouth pursued so many different channels that no one of them could be identified as the true river. By this time, of course, Mackenzie was well aware that the sea into which it emptied was not the Pacific but the Arctic or as it was then called, the Hyperborean Sea.

In spite of his disappointment he resolved to spend as much time as he dared, considering the dwindling provisions, in observing the nature of the country and its inhabitants. He noticed that the willow trees here were dwarfed to three feet; that the nearby land was covered with short grass and flowers though thawed not more than four inches below the surface. On top, the soil turned to slime under the bright sun but a few inches beneath, all was solid ice.

He and his men found remains of many Eskimo camps where the occupants had left sled runners, sinew and willow-bark cording, small pieces of flint fixed into wooden handles for knives and, most amazing of all, a square stone kettle with a flat bottom capable of holding two gallons.

The possibility of meeting Eskimos face to face so alarmed Mackenzie's Indians that he knew they would have left him if they had dared. He wrote:

I satisfied them in some degree by the assurance that I would proceed onward but seven days more and, if I did not get to the sea, I would return. Indeed, the low state of the provisions, without any other consideration, formed a very sufficient security for the maintenance of my agreement.

Before the seven days ended, the party came to the shore of the flat land and saw stretching before them the vast expanse of Arctic ice. The rise and fall of the tide also proved that they had indeed reached an ocean though not the one they sought. Mackenzie's journal says:

> We landed at the boundary of our voyage in this direction.

He had a wooden post erected on which he carved his name, the latitude and the number of persons in his party.

A day or so after their arrival, someone saw great white fish in the open water not far from land. Mackenzie recognized from their size that they must be whales and with great enthusiasm he and several men took after them in a canoe. When fog suddenly closed down all around them, he realized, as he later wrote,

> It was indeed a very wild and unreflecting enterprise and it was a very fortunate circumstance that we failed in our attempt to overtake them.

Thankfully, they managed to reach the shore.

On Thursday, July 16, forty-two days after they had left Fort Chipewyan, the party started back up the river. The hunters brought in two reindeer,

> which proved a very seasonable supply as our pemmican

had become mouldy for some time past, though in that situation we were under the necessity of eating it.

Cranberries and yellow raspberries, with other plants and herbs, also appeared in abundance.

The return through the spreading delta required six days, then the flotilla once more found the main channel of the river. Now, however, the current was against them. They had to tow the canoes with lines, work so exhausting that the men labored in two-hour shifts, then fell to the ground while others went on with the towing.

The journey became a race with time and hunger. The short Arctic summer was drawing to a close; the weather was usually cold and rainy, though broken by short periods of intense heat. Always, they moved through clouds of tormenting mosquitoes and black flies so thick they looked like fur on the men's hands and faces. On Saturday, August 22, they reached the entrance of Great Slave Lake, again swept by terrific storms. The canoes had several narrow escapes from capsizing; one ran on a stump and was so badly damaged it filled with water and was with difficulty dragged out for repair.

With the coming of September, freezing weather and snow added to their misery but the voyage was nearing its end. Saturday, the twelfth, they camped on the shore of their home lake, Athabasca, and as usual for homecomings got out every bit of ribbon, every bright handkerchief and every banner, no matter how tattered. The men washed and put on their best clothes and at three o'clock on Sunday afternoon, with a bold dash, swept up to the dock at Fort Chipewyan.

Usually, the appearance of a brigade of any kind brought the whole population of the fort to the dock in a shouting mob, throwing their caps into the air, yelling and shooting off firearms.

Today the five men building a new storehouse looked up but gave no other sign of having seen the arrival. Nobody came from inside the post. Everywhere was silence as if nothing had happened.

Alexander must have been terribly hurt but his lifelong habit of self-discipline saved him. He gave no sign of being disturbed, only hastened to ask where Roderick was. Learning that he had gone with the last fur brigade to Grand Portage and that in his place was Mr. McLeod, one of the partners closest to McTavish, he understood the indifference of the fort. He was being deliberately punished for having gone exploring contrary to McTavish's wishes.

To the men the letdown was severe. They had survived a difficult journey of three thousand miles, they were bone weary and hungry but no one cared. Like whipped curs they straggled back to work.

Even in his journal, Mackenzie restrained his feelings, writing only:

> We concluded this voyage, which had occupied the considerable space of one hundred and two days.

One can guess his inner frustration by his naming of the river he had found, "River of Disappointment." Later geographers thought better of it and christened it the Mackenzie, with the added descriptive phrase, "The Mississippi of the North."

Wasting no time in self-pity, Mackenzie wrote to his cousin:

> This voyage has settled the dubious point of a practicable North-West passage; and I trust it has set that long-agitated question at rest and extinguished the disputes respecting it forever.

He did not add, as he might have, that it also extinguished

hope of anyone's winning the prize of twenty thousand pounds which had been a standing offer of the British government for a proved discovery of such a passage. So, after nine years of constant effort, one part of Mackenzie's great dream had died. It was, however, not in his nature to sulk over defeat. If Simon McTavish imagined he had crushed his ambitious young partner he was greatly mistaken. At once Alexander turned to his second ambition, a journey to the Pacific Ocean.

3

MACKENZIE had discovered one of the largest rivers on the American continent. The Mackenzie drains an area of over six hundred and seventy thousand square miles. With its main tributary, the Peace, it runs for two thousand, five hundred miles from the northern Rocky Mountains to the Arctic Ocean. Its discovery opened an unbelievably rich fur-producing area, yet Simon McTavish stubbornly maintained his disinterest.

The next spring when he and Mackenzie met at Grand Portage he complained of the few furs coming down from the Athabasca district, a dig at Alexander. Also, he and some of the other partners chose to ignore their colleague's recent voyage. Writing back to Roderick, Alexander said: "My expedition was hardly spoken of but that is what I expected." Others of the company held a different view. They took Mackenzie's part and ascribed McTavish's attitude to jealousy. There were enough of them to vote Alexander time off to prepare and conduct his next proposed exploration though allowing him no funds. He would have to use his own money, recruit his own men and carry through the endeavor as a private affair. This did not trouble Mackenzie. By this time his dedication to his chosen work was so complete that nothing could stop him. To replenish his funds he continued as a trader at Fort Chipewyan for one more year. Then, to learn what he needed of astronomy and to secure suitable instruments for taking observations, he left his post for a year's study in England.

He was a handsome young man nearing thirty years of age and welcome in many a fine London home but he reports in his journal: "I made myself but little known during my residence in London, the winter of 1791-2." Again the pretty girls were set aside for a man's dream of adventure. Moreover, he heard enough of the voyages being sponsored by the Spanish as well as the British to feel that the destiny of the North American continent hung in the balance. Time grew short.

He left England for the return trip early in April, 1792, only a month before the mysterious River of the West would be found and named the Columbia, not by an Englishman or a Spaniard but by Captain Robert Gray, an American. This achievement brought a third country into the race for the Pacific Coast.

Word of the discovery was slow in reaching England and Mackenzie probably did not hear of it for several years. He already surmised from writings of English and Spanish explorers that all suspected the presence of a very large river somewhere in the neighborhood of forty-six degrees, north latitude. This must be the river of Carver's book.

From his first exploration, Mackenzie had learned that a chain of high mountains stood between Lake Athabasca and the ocean. He had admired their jagged outline against the western sky. He had also become interested in the Peace River which he had seen only on its lower stretches. Undoubtedly, he reasoned, it rose in those western mountains, Carver's high point of land in the middle of the continent, though possibly it was farther to the west than he had thought. It seemed reasonable, therefore, that if one ascended this river to its source one might be able to cross to the other side of that mountain range and reach the headwaters of the fabled Oregon. Once having found it, all that would be needed was to follow it to the sea.

There was no time to lose. As soon as he reached Canada, Mackenzie hastened to Grand Portage for the annual meeting of the partners in August; then on to Fort Chipewyan, a two-months' journey. He had sent word ahead that a small party of men was to go up the Peace beyond the most distant settlement of the company, and there prepare timbers for a house. Here, at an elevation of four thousand feet and one hundred and fifty miles from the foot of the Rockies, he planned to spend the winter, to be ready for the dash to the Pacific as soon as spring came. Once more, Roderick agreed to take charge of Fort Chipewyan while he was gone.

For the first stage of the journey, Mackenzie took a large crew of men and moved along rapidly though the weather was cold and raw. They were working against time since ice might appear in the Peace any day. After this, it would be difficult, perhaps impossible, to travel at all. They left Fort Chipewyan on October 10, 1792, and on the 19th, reached the "Old Establishment," where another Nor'wester, James Finlay, was in charge.

They could stop no longer than for a night's rest, and next morning went on, with the enthusiastic send-off of the entire population, some three hundred men. Their final destination was six miles farther up the Peace, where they set up winter camp with about seventy men, many of them Indians, to spend the cold months hunting and trading.

They arrived none too soon as ice began to run in the river and all navigation ended until late the next April. The cold became so severe that the axes of the workmen turned almost as brittle as glass. On December 2, Mackenzie's Fahrenheit thermometer was broken, so from then on no accurate record of the temperature could be kept.

Very cold weather and deep snow were followed by a phenomenon he had never before observed. As he tells it:

> The wind being at northeast, and the weather calm and cloudy, a rumbling noise was heard in the air like distant thunder, when the sky cleared away in the south-west; from whence there blew a perfect hurricane which lasted till eight. Soon after it commenced, the atmosphere became so warm that it dissolved all the snow on the ground; even the ice was covered with water and had the same appearance as when it is breaking up in the spring.

So he recorded his first Chinook, the famous warm wind of the Northwest, which still surprises those experiencing it for the first time.

Mackenzie's winter camp soon gathered many Indians, come to trade furs for the white man's goods. It was his first experience of living among them and he was shocked at the treatment given their women.

> It is not uncommon while the men carry nothing but a gun, that their wives and daughters follow with such weighty burdens that if they lay them down they cannot replace them and that is a kindness which the men will not deign to perform, so that during their journeys they are frequently obliged to lean against a tree for a small portion of temporary relief.

On April 20, he noted that the "summer companions," gnats and mosquitoes, had arrived. Suddenly, among the towering pines and spruces, birch and cottonwood trees budded and flowers covered the ground where a few days before, had been only ice and snow. The time for the big dash was at hand. Mackenzie packed up the winter's catch of furs, six canoe loads, and sent them back to Fort Chipewyan with his reports and dispatches for the partners at Grand Portage.

He had had all winter to pick the men to accompany him to the Pacific. This time, he resolved not to be encumbered with whole families of Indians who would be frightened and want to turn back. He chose only ten men, so all could go in one canoe. For his assistant and next in command, he again selected the Scot, Alexander McKay, who had accompanied him on the first voyage; six canoemen, two of whom had also been with him the previous trip, and two young Indians, employed as hunters and interpreters. He also took along his dog, though no mention of the animal's name is made in his journal.

He had given careful attention to the building of the canoe. It was made of birchbark, twenty-five feet long, exclusive of the curves of stem and stern, twenty-six inches deep with a four-foot, nine-inch beam; a large vessel of its kind, yet so light that two men could carry her on a good road three or four miles without resting. This slender craft could transport three thousand pounds of weight, including the men, provisions, goods for presents, arms, ammunition and baggage.

Mackenzie left two men in charge of the camp and on May 9, 1792, started on the voyage toward which all his energies had been devoted for thirteen years. At first, everything went well. The Peace, a mighty stream, flowed through beautiful country where mountains, rising from mere hills to tremendous height, crowded one another in all directions, thrusting their great pine-clad shoulders into the sky. Eight days later, much sooner than expected, the men could see in a southwesterly direction, the snow-covered peaks of the Rockies, glittering in the spring sunshine.

As they progressed into the mountains, their real troubles began. The canoe struck a submerged stump and was badly damaged. The banks were so steep, there was no place to unload her except one small spot, but here a two-hour repair job enabled them to go on.

Series after series of rapids, cascades and falls caused constant traverses from one side of the stream to the other, often with great danger. Frequently the current was too swift for paddling and the men had to tow the canoe with a line which sometimes stretched to three hundred and fifty feet. To lighten the craft, all the men not actively towing climbed along the bank and Mackenzie writes:

> I could not but reflect, with infinite anxiety, on the hazard of my enterprise; one false step of those pulling the line, or breaking of the line itself, would have consigned the canoe and everything in it to instant destruction.

In addition to the terrors of the river was the danger from rocks that constantly rolled down from above. At one place, in order to walk along the steep bank, Mackenzie himself cut steps in it for a distance of twenty feet, dug in his knife to keep from slipping into the river, then leaped to a small rock below. Once there,

> I received those who followed me on my shoulders. In this manner four of us passed and dragged up the canoe, in which attempt we broke her.

Again they must stop for repairs. These consisted of putting in new ribs, patching the holes with pieces of bark secured by sewing with sinew, and calking with the gum of pine and spruce trees. Each repair added to the weight of the canoe, making the frequent portages more and more difficult.

In one place, where the water was too swift for paddling and too deep for poling, the men towing the craft had to pass on the outside of trees that grew on the edge of the precipice. Another time, the person tying up the canoe failed to make it fast and the current swung it away. Fortunately, one man, from sheer fatigue, had dropped to the ground with the end of the line still in his hand, and so saved the craft. Carrying it around rapids and falls was so frequent that one day Mackenzie records unloading and reloading her four times in two miles, yet he refused to be discouraged.

Finally, despite all his determination, he saw it was impractical to continue in the canoe. The river was one boiling rage of rapids, falls and cross currents where no craft could live. His men begged him to leave off this suicidal endeavor and return to Fort Chipewyan. Deeply discouraged, Mackenzie took two men with him and climbed the steep slope from the river to a point where he could see downstream for some miles. Nothing ahead but rapids and falls. Through the thick pine forest and undergrowth of vines and bushes they cut their way for miles along the cliffs. At length, far below and ahead, the river calmed enough so a canoe could run it. Back went Mackenzie to his waiting crew.

"This won't be so bad. We'll just go over the top for a few miles."

"Over the top? You mean, carry the canoe up this mountain? It can't be done."

Mackenzie dug an axe out of his pack. "Ordinary fellows might have trouble but we can do it."

He never asked of his men anything he would not do himself. Up the mountain he started, directing them to cut the trees in such a way that they fell along one side and formed a parapet at the edge of the cliff. Then they warped the canoe up by doubling the line around stumps and trees to get more pull. The first day they made three miles, three the next and four the third.

"You see?" Mackenzie pointed down to the river, running free and clear.

The expedition was now traveling through the heart of the northern Rocky Mountain Range, with peaks rising all about them six to nine thousand feet in height. The days were hot, the nights very cold. On May 31, they came to a fork in the stream. One branch, now called the Finlay, came in from west-northwest and the other, named the Parsnip from the wild parsnips growing near by, entered from south-southeast. Mackenzie's impulse was to take the north one as most likely to lead to the Pacific. An old Indian warned him against this, saying this branch was soon lost in many small streams. By following the Parsnip they would arrive at a carrying place which led to another large, west-flowing stream. Reluctantly Mackenzie followed the old man's advice and for almost two weeks the men beat their way up the dwindling Parsnip. Here, on June 12, they came to a lake which Mackenzie judged must be the source of the Peace River system. Sure enough, here was a well-trodden carrying place which led to a second small lake and a trickle of water starting west. They had crossed the divide.

The stream increased rapidly and soon became a torrent. By the end of each day the men were numb from constant wading waist-deep in glacier run-off. Their unwilling guide again began to talk of going home. One day they got into such terrific rapids that the canoe was whirled around and around with no possibility of controlling it. A few more spins and it was flung out against a rock, smashed flat. Miraculously, none of the men had been lost and now, using the flattened boat as a raft, they paddled gingerly to shore and took stock of their damages. A few packs of goods were gone and practically all their stock of lead bullets.

At this, Mackenzie reports, the men were so discouraged they sat down and wept. This was the end. They would surely desert him now and who could blame them? All the years of his dreaming and striving would be lost.

Here Mackenzie reveals the strength and greatness of character he had been building since boyhood. He did not scold his men. Instead, he ordered camp made in a comfortable spot and a good meal cooked. What matter if he did use up a lot of the dwindling stores on this one dinner? The whole expedition hung upon its success.

After dinner, when all were warm and relaxed, he began talking quietly and sympathetically of their problem, yet never forgetting to dwell on their pride. It was an honor to conquer disaster, he said. If they went home as failures, no one would let them forget it. Northmen had a reputation for courage and resolution in the face of disaster.

He then played his trump card. Without raising his voice he declared that regardless of what others did, he was going on to the Pacific Ocean, alone if necessary. It was a bold gamble, but Mackenzie won. Somewhat shamefaced, his men assured him they had never meant to leave him. Wherever he went, they would go with him.

On further study, the old canoe was not as hopeless as it had seemed. Once more they patched it up and applied pine gum to cracks and breaks in the birchbark. It had now become so heavy from continued repairs that it took six men to carry it.

On June 18, Mackenzie had his first taste of triumph. The little stream they had been following emptied into a large, furious river called by the Indians the Tacoutche Tesse. We know it as the Fraser. Mackenzie felt sure this was the stream he had been seeking, the longed-for River of the West, the Oregon. He had not yet heard the name Columbia.

Perhaps he felt a bit disappointed when he first saw it. Running in a deep trench between mountain ranges, it looked narrow and had an ugly yellow color from the quantities of silt it carried. It had taken its rise one hundred and fifty miles to the south, at the foot of mighty Mt. Robson, whose majestic, snow-covered head looks down from its twelve thousand, nine hundred and seventy-two feet upon all other peaks in the Canadian Rockies, where at least twenty-one within Jasper and Banff National Parks are over ten thousand feet high. So far it had been flowing north but here it curled around the end of the Cariboo Range into another narrow trough and headed for the sea.

Now the canoemen began to learn something about speed. The great fall in the river bed sends the Fraser charging along at a breakneck rate with no time to recover from one rapids until another begins. In what is now called Fort George Canyon the canoe was wrecked again. Indians who gathered along the shore, expressing hostility until MacKenzie convinced them with gifts that he meant no harm, told him that the river did not go west but toward the midday sun. At its mouth were white men who lived in houses made of wood. However, he must be warned that canoes could not go much farther.

After all he had undergone, Mackenzie now began to have doubts of his success. Perhaps this was not the river he thought. Perhaps it never did reach the ocean but emptied into a great lake, as the Peace River did. He had come to a time of decision. Two months of the short summer season were gone. He had only thirty days' provisions left and game was so scarce they could not count on much of it. They had only one hundred and fifty bullets and thirty pounds of shot which might conceivably be melted into bullets.

There was one alternative to following this angry river. For days, Indians had been telling him of a small stream some distance back that did come in from the west. If he followed that, he would reach the ocean in a few days' time. But to have to give up his exploration of the Great River of the West, on which his heart had been set for so many years! To acknowledge to his men that he was defeated!

Again Mackenzie proved the greatness of his character. Concealing his bitter disappointment, he announced his decision and ordered McKay to carve his name and the date on a tree to mark the southernmost point to which they had gone, now called Alexandria. Then back up the Tacoutche they took their weary march, the men again pleading to go home. Mackenzie's own despair became so deep he once had to go off by himself for a night alone to regain his composure. How, once again, to bend his men to his will? He decided the answer lay in action. They needed something constructive to do. The old canoe was hopeless, so they would build a new one.

When they finished it, on July 1, it was such an obvious improvement over the old one, it gave the men a sense of pride and accomplishment. Their worst discomfort at this camp was sand flies of which Mackenzie wrote, "I am disposed to consider it the most tormenting insect of its size in nature."

Two days later they reached the small river of which the Indians had told them, now called the Blackwater, which they now began to follow. At its mouth they dug a cache and concealed part of their meager supplies for the return trip. A few days more and they could no longer use the canoe in the shallow stream. They built a stage on which to place it, upside down, shaded by a covering of small trees and branches to prevent its drying out and cracking. Near it they also hid everything else they could possibly discard. Rations were cut to two meals a day. Even so, each man was heavily loaded when, on July 4, they started on foot to find the ocean. In addition to his share of the food supplies, Mackenzie carried his telescope slung across his shoulders.

They met more and more Indians, some friendly and some hostile. One tribe would help them along for a few days; another drove them away with guns. These were fish-eating Indians and Mackenzie discovered they were very superstitious, believing anything of animal origin would frighten away the salmon. One of his men had eaten venison and tossed a bone into the river, whereupon a native dived in after it, threw it into the fire and washed his polluted hands. When the pet dog, which had gone with them all this way, was seen gnawing a bone, the Indians chased it away and it was lost.

Mackenzie knew they must be near the sea. The air smelled of it. On July 18 they came to Indian houses where were articles of European manufacture. He wrote triumphantly in his journal:

> From these houses I could perceive the termination of
> the river and its discharge into a narrow arm of the sea.

This stream, now called the Bella Coola, enters South Bentinck arm of Dean Channel approximately one hundred miles above the head of Vancouver Island. Though the rise and fall of the tide was obvious, the party was still some miles from the ocean but on Saturday, July 20, they borrowed a leaky canoe and got out into the bay where they landed in a small cove on the right or north side. For two days they cruised around looking for a place to take an observation for latitude and longitude.

Here they were intercepted by very hostile Indians who said a large canoe of white men had visited them lately and that *Macubah* had fired on them and *Bensins* had struck one man with the flat of his sword. Probably deserved it, thought

Mackenzie, who correctly understood the names as those of George Vancouver and Menzies, the botanist on his ship. He had missed them by only a few weeks. What a meeting it might have been!

After an uneasy night spent on a great rock, Mackenzie dared no longer risk the growing hostility of the Indians. He mixed vermillion and melted grease and wrote in bold letters on the southeast face of the rock, "Alexander Mackenzie, from Canada, by land, the twenty-second of July, one thousand seven hundred and ninety-three."

His great ambition had been fulfilled. Still the self-contained man, he wrote no glowing words of his feelings at this great moment. Perhaps his immediate problems gave him no time since he was now faced with the almost hopeless task of getting back home with all his party alive. Added to the scarcity of food was the men's state of health. One of the Indian hunters was very sick and so weak he could not walk; all had taken terrible colds. Mackenzie's daily struggle was to keep the men who were fit from hurrying on by themselves. Over and over he assured them he had no further ambition but to protect them and see them safely back at Fort Chipewyan. Day by day he had to persuade them all over again to stay with him and help carry the sick man.

The day they found their lost dog was a turning point. The poor starved animal seemed crazed and did not recognize them. After several days of food and petting, he once more accepted them as friends, barking joyfully and leaping from one to another. This seemed an assurance of a safe return home.

On July 28 they reached their hidden canoe and found it unharmed, a bit of good luck which moved Mackenzie to give generous presents to the neighboring Indians. When they once more reached the divide and were back on the Peace River, the going was easier, but Mackenzie never gave up his habit of observing everything about the country. He wrote:

> If I could have spared the time and been able to exert myself, for I was afflicted with a swelling in my ankles so that I could not walk but with great pain and difficulty, it was my intention to have taken some salmon alive and colonized them in the Peace River, though it is doubtful that fish would live in waters that have not a communication with the sea.

Thus did he anticipate attempts of modern fisheries to transplant salmon.

At last came the moment of triumph with their return to their winter camp on Peace River. The date was Saturday, August 24, and Mackenzie describes it thus:

> At length, as we rounded a point and came in view of the fort, we threw out a flag and accompanied it with a general discharge of fire-arms; while the men were in such spirits and made such an active use of their paddles that we arrived before the two men whom we left here in the spring could recover their senses to answer us. Thus we landed at four in the afternoon at the place which we left on the 9th of May.

They could not stay here, however, but went on:

> After an absence of eleven months, I arrived at Fort Chipewyan, where I remained, for the purposes of trade, during the succeeding winter.

Thus ends Mackenzie's account of the momentous journey. As he had promised Roderick, once he had reached the Pacific Ocean, he planned no more explorations for himself. Further search for the Great River of the West would have to be carried out by someone else, though he would never cease to promote such a search. All his thoughts turned toward the head of the North West Company, Simon McTavish. Surely, now that he, Mackenzie, had reached the ocean and had gone partway down the river which he believed to be the fabled Oregon, the company would go ahead to secure it for Great Britain and its own trade.

For six more years Mackenzie continued with the North Westers, faithfully performing his duties as a partner and trying to bring the others to his views. Finding that McTavish still would not yield an inch, he quit the company and went home to Scotland. There he wrote his famous book, *Voyages from Montreal on the River St. Lawrence Through the Continent of North America to the Frozen and Pacific Oceans in the Years 1789 and 1793.*

It became an immediate success and Mackenzie was knighted for his achievements. His later activities belong to another story when Simon Fraser, also a partner in the North West Company, enters the scene to complete the work Mackenzie began.

THE SECOND ROAD

Lewis and Clark, 1805–1806

I

ONE day in 1793, the same summer when Alexander Mackenzie and his hardy crew were making their dash to the Pacific Ocean, a caller came to Monticello, the Virginia home of Secretary of State Thomas Jefferson. He was a tall, dark, slender youth whom Jefferson recognized as Meriwether Lewis, son of a neighbor, the Widow Marks, who owned the plantation called Locust Hill. He invited the young man into his study.

"Kind of you to call, Meriwether."

"A bit presumptuous, perhaps, Mr. Jefferson. I know you must be very busy, when you are home from Washington for such a brief visit."

"Not too busy to talk to my neighbors. Your mother is well, I hope?"

"Yes, sir, very well, though sad over the death of my step-father last year."

"I was sorry to hear of that. You are now managing the plantation for her, they tell me. You didn't go to college, then?"

"No, sir. I had planned to enter William and Mary this year but it seemed to me I was needed here. But I find the plantation is going along very well, nothing my brother Reuben can't handle, so I—I have a favor to ask of you, if I may."

43

"Why, certainly, though I can't tell until I hear it whether I can grant it."

A flush came into the tanned young face. "Mr. Jefferson, I know I shall never care much for plantation life. I want more action. Especially, I want to go to the West, out into Kentucky and Ohio, and even beyond the Mississippi. I heard that the American Philosophical Society, of which you are president, I believe, is planning to send an expedition up the Missouri. I'd like to be one of the party."

Thomas Jefferson leaned back in his chair and smiled. "So you, also, have the Western urge. It must be in the air."

"I guess so, sir. I get to thinking about it and feel I must go. All that country beyond the Mississippi and no one has even seen it, or knows how big it is."

Jefferson shook his head slowly. "I feel the same way, but I'm fifty years old. By the way, I've lately come across a very interesting map, tucked away in a Congressional file. It was drawn a few years ago by a man named Peter Pond. He was a partner in the North West Company, that group of Canadian fur traders, though he was an American by birth. When his own company showed no interest in his map and ideas, he brought them to our Congress. I am sorry to say that there they have met much the same fate, so far.

"Pond's map shows a great river flowing into the Pacific, but much too far north for the Columbia, that our Captain Robert Gray discovered—at least the mouth of it—last year. You've heard of the achievement, I trust."

"Oh, yes, sir. Named it the Columbia for his ship, didn't he? Very exciting news."

"Indeed it is. The Great River of the West, that explorers have been searching out for years. And to think it was an American who found it!"

"Where do Peter Pond and his map come into it?"

Jefferson leaned forward, his voice low and earnest. "Peter Pond was wrong in his geography but he had a great idea. He proposed establishing a trading base at the mouth of the River of the West, to supply inland posts from the Pacific, instead of by the long overland trip from Montreal. It sounds so sensible, I wonder that the North West Company has never put it into effect."

"Perhaps it's lucky for us they haven't," said Lewis. "Doesn't Captain Gray's discovery give us Americans a claim to that river?"

"It certainly does but the British also have a claim. Captain George Vancouver reached the mouth of the Columbia only four months after Gray. He sent a small ship, under Lieutenant Broughton, one hundred miles up the river. We need to do something to counteract that claim."

"Does this proposed expedition up the Missouri have anything to do with such counteraction?" Meriwether asked, a sly twinkle in his eye.

Jefferson laughed. "You understand a great deal, for your age." Then he sobered and leaned across the desk to look into the younger man's equally sober face. "Some day, Meriwether, I foresee that all the country from the Mississippi to the Pacific will be part of the United States, though I do not know when or how this will come about. If we could find a river route by way of the Missouri and Columbia, we would have a natural waterway across the continent—the old dream of the Northwest Passage, only farther south than anyone has looked for it."

The range of Jefferson's imagination startled young Lewis. "So you think the two rivers rise close together, one flowing east and the other west?"

"I believe so, though it is not an original thought with me. I first read it more than ten years ago, in a book written by an explorer named Jonathan Carver. According to him there may be no more than a short portage, perhaps a day's journey or less, between the headwaters of the two rivers."

"But Spain owns Louisiana. Would she let us go through her territory?"

"Perhaps not, though we only want to study the geography of the region, and find out whether there is a northern tributary of the Missouri which comes close to the Saskatchewan in Canada. If so, we might work out a trade agreement with Spain and Great Britain for shipping Canadian furs to the seaboard by way of the Missouri and the Ohio, which are free of ice almost the year round. It would be cheaper for the Canadians than overland to Montreal, provide us with commerce and give Spain part of the profits."

"A brilliant plan, Mr. Jefferson."

"Told to you in confidence, you understand."

"Certainly, sir."

Mr. Jefferson's mood changed. "How old are you, Meriwether? The years slip by so fast, I can't remember."

"Nineteen, sir."

"Now about this expedition—it is only in the planning stage and I am not sure it will really develop. But even if it does"—he looked straight into the eager young eyes—"I am sorry, but I could hardly choose you in preference to others who have had years of experience in the wilderness and in handling men. You are still very young and have never been west of the Alleghenies, have you?"

Meriwether's head drooped. "No, sir."

"Give yourself time to prepare. Your chance will come."

"Thank you, Mr. Jefferson." Meriwether turned away, deeply disappointed though he could see the justice of the decision. For a moment, he wished he had gone to college with his other young friends, though the thought of being cooped up in class-rooms for hours each day was distasteful. He loved the fields and woods, but managing a plantation was almost as confining as college.

For another year, he stuck faithfully to his self-imposed task, then joined the Army. He received a commission as ensign, at that time an Army rank, and served under General Anthony Wayne in a series of campaigns through Kentucky, Tennessee and Ohio.

During these years, he made friends with another young officer, four years older than himself. Captain William Clark had fiery-red hair and whiskers and was even more of a confirmed woodsman than Meriwether Lewis. Comparing notes, they found they both were Virginia born, and that Clark was a younger brother of the Revolutionary hero, George Rogers Clark.

He lacked the formal education Meriwether Lewis had re-ceived but, having grown up in a family where prominent men were frequent visitors, he had listened to their talk and had received informal instruction, besides making many friends.

After the Revolution his family had left Virginia, floating down the Ohio River on a flatboat to a new home at Louisville, Kentucky, where they now lived on a plantation named Mul-berry Hill.

Meriwether Lewis fell under the spell of this red-headed young man, who in turn respected the superior intellect and calm reasoning power of Lewis. They became such friends as seldom find one another and throughout their years of close association, no difference ever arose between them.

Lewis often thought of Thomas Jefferson, and wondered at his own brashness in going to see him, when he was only nineteen years old. When Jefferson was elected President, Captain Lewis, in faraway Detroit, thought proudly, "He was my neighbor and friend."

Then, one day, a surprising letter came to the captain. Thomas Jefferson invited him to become his own private secretary. To think that this great man remembered him! Not only that, but had watched his development and approved of him so much that his letter said:

> Your knowledge of the Western country, of the Army, and of all its interests and relations has rendered it desirable for public as well as private purposes that you should be engaged in that office.

A glow of pleasure flowed through Meriwether Lewis's lithe young frame. He had been preparing himself, he was ready for anything. He cared not that the salary in the offered position was only five hundred dollars per year. He would live in the executive mansion, eat his meals with Jefferson's own family, meet all the great men who came to see the President. He could also retain his military rank.

He accepted the invitation at once and for two years lived a very different life from that of the army camp. Diplomats, representatives of foreign countries, Congressmen and many other visitors of note were his daily companions. Jefferson entrusted him with intimate knowledge of all the affairs of state, once even sending him to convey his annual message to the Senate, when he did not wish to appear in person.

Most important of all to Meriwether Lewis was Jefferson's continuing interest in that idea of exploring the Missouri and finding the way down the Columbia to the sea. The expedition for which Meriwether had offered himself years before had not come off, after all, but Jefferson still talked of the idea.

One day he drew his secretary into his private office and closed the door. "Meriwether, the time has come. Look at this. I just received it from England."

He laid on the table a book, *Voyages from Montreal on the River St. Lawrence Through the Continent of North America to the Frozen and Pacific Oceans.* The author was Sir Alexander Mackenzie.

Lewis wrinkled his forehead. "Wasn't he one of those North West Company men? A Canadian fur trader?"

"He was. The first man to reach the Pacific Ocean by land, nearly ten years ago. He has been in England but now I understand he has returned to Canada, head of a new fur company. I am reliably informed he is the most powerful man in the entire business. What he plans will undoubtedly be carried out. Read the conclusion of the book, Meriwether."

The secretary's eyes ran rapidly over the final paragraphs, picking up significant bits:

> By opening this intercourse between the Atlantic and Pacific . . . forming regular establishments through the interior and at both extremes . . . the entire command of the fur trade of North America . . . from 48 degrees to the pole . . . many political reasons, which it is not necessary here to enumerate, must present themselves . . .

"Why, they are planning to take over the whole Columbia area for Great Britain."

"Exactly so, unless we stop them. The French own Louisiana now. I think they will give us permission to go through their territory. Napoleon is so busy in Europe, he hasn't time to be worried about Louisiana. Are you ready to undertake an expedition up the Missouri and down the Columbia to the sea?"

"Mr. President, I have been ready for ten years."

"Figure how much it will cost, while I prepare a message to Congress."

On January 18, 1803, President Jefferson sent to Congress a private message on Indian trade and the western country and asked for an appropriation of two thousand, five hundred dollars, the amount Meriwether Lewis had estimated necessary. Impressed by the facts the President gave them, Congressmen made the appropriation and agreed to Mr. Jefferson's choice of Lewis to lead the expedition.

"I shall need someone to share the responsibility," Lewis insisted. "Suppose something should happen to me. Who would carry on the effort?'

"Whom would you suggest?"

Lewis knew exactly the man he wanted, William Clark, who had lately retired from the Army and given up his captain's commission.

"We'll get a new commission for him," the President promised.

"There is no one else I should like to have as well as you," Lewis wrote to his friend.

"There is no man with whom I should rather serve," Clark replied.

Lewis admitted he knew little or nothing of astronomy, and the use of instruments for observing latitude and longitude, or of map making. To acquire these skills he spent part of the year studying in Philadelphia.

In the fall of 1803, he journeyed down the Ohio, met Clark, and set up a camp across the Mississippi from St. Louis where they went about their final preparations for the trip. Clark attended to the purchase of boats and supplies, leaving Lewis the task of selecting the men. Jefferson had suggested a party of ten or twelve, but the two captains soon decided they would need more than twice that number. They hoped to sail well up the Missouri in a large keelboat which, in itself, would require a sizable crew. Then there must be smaller boats for the latter stages of the journey.

They had many applicants and used care in choosing those who would make up a well-balanced crew. A Frenchman named Drouillard, commonly pronounced Drewyer, was chosen because of his experience as plainsman, riverman, hunter, trapper and master of Indian sign language. Pierre Cruzatte, though blind in one eye and with poor vision in the other, was, of all the party, the best at handling a boat. He also carried with him his fiddle, which enlivened many evenings and perhaps did more than anything else to lift the morale of the other men during long, dull evenings in camp.

John Shields was a good blacksmith and kept the guns in repair. Bratton could tinker and fix anything else that went wrong. Then there was George Shannon.

He came to Lewis's tent one day late in the fall, a handsome, black-haired, blue-eyed boy, gaunt from hunger.

"Captain Lewis, sir, I should like to enlist in your expedition."

The boy's language was not that of the rough rivermen.

"Shannon? From Virginia?"

"Yes, sir, until we migrated to Ohio."

"You come of good family, Shannon. I remember your father. Did he send you to enlist with me?"

The boy's head dropped. "He is dead, sir. Last winter he was lost in the woods and froze to death."

"I am sorry to hear that. Then did your mother permit you to come?"

"No, sir. She sent me to Pittsburg to go to school but I—"

"Ran away?"

"Not exactly, sir. I just came without permission."

"How old are you, Shannon?"

"Well, sir, I'm not quite eighteen yet, but—"

"How much under eighteen?"

The boy's voice could hardly be heard. "Eighteen months under, sir."

"In other words, you are sixteen."

"Yes, sir." He lifted his head and eyes desperate with longing looked into Lewis's. "Oh, Captain, sir, I do so want to go."

Of all the men who had presented themselves, Shannon probably was least qualified for the journey, yet somehow Lewis felt himself drawn to the boy. Perhaps he remembered how he had felt, at nineteen, when he applied to Thomas Jefferson for a chance to go on that expedition that never came off.

"I could count on you to expect no favors because of your youth? You would take your turn at the dirty work like everyone else?"

"Sir, I would die before I would complain."

"I believe you would, Shannon. How long since you have eaten?"

"Three days, sir."

"Go tell Captain Clark to enlist you as a private and give you something to eat."

"Oh, thank you, sir." The boy was off like a shot.

Lewis shook his head. "I wonder," he asked himself, "how many times I shall regret taking him? But somehow I could not say no to him."

Since, in the eyes of Congress, this was a military expedition, the men received army rations during that winter, enabling Lewis to stretch his twenty-five hundred dollars farther. He still found it insufficient to buy the amount of red flannel and calico, medals cast with the impression of President Jefferson on one side, small United States flags, gaudy coats of blue and scarlet, trimmed with bright brass buttons, for presents to important

Indian chiefs, plus guns and ammunition and plentiful supplies of pemmican. His funds appear to have been supplemented by the President himself, as no further appropriations were asked of Congress.

By early spring of 1804, everything was ready. Clark had secured a keelboat fifty-five feet long, shallow draft, square-rigged sail and twenty-two oars. A tow-line was fastened to her mast pole to track her upstream through rapids. In addition, there were two pirogues, sharp-prowed, wide-sterned boats shaped something like flatirons; one red, the other white. Six men were required to row the first, nine the second. Sails were supplied for use when the wind was right.

A crew of twenty-seven was augmented by eight or nine temporary employees who would bring the keelboat back from winter quarters.

Lewis had received his passports from the French governor in St. Louis since his party would be traveling through French territory as far as the Rocky Mountains. He lacked only the final letter of instruction from President Jefferson. Why was it so long in coming?

2

TOWARD the end of April, Lewis stepped out of his tent one morning to see Captain Clark coming up from the river, dejection written all over his rugged features.

"No boat yet?"

Clark shook his head. "And the weather perfect. We should have been on our way a week ago. Why do we have to wait any longer? Didn't the President give you full instructions before you left Washington last fall?

"In general, yes, but I was told to wait here for final word.

For some time I have had a feeling that something important has happened since we left home. More than a year ago, when the President sent Mr. Monroe to France, the only reason he gave was that he wanted to buy New Orleans from Napoleon, so our traders could get out into the Gulf of Mexico without having to pay tribute to French agents there. Somehow, that did not seem a big enough reason for a special ambassador. Mr. Livingston, our regular ambassador, could have handled such a negotiation."

"But what else could be in his mind?"

"I have an idea," said Lewis slowly, "but I dare not mention it even to you, until word comes. We must wait here. Keep the men busy. They are getting restless."

Day after day, as May came in and the fine weather continued, Clark put the men through their drills but every day he could see rebellion growing within them. Would the final word from the President never come?

On the afternoon of May 13, there seemed to be unusual activity across the Mississippi around the St. Louis docks. Then smoke rolled up from a tall stack and a steamboat appeared below the city.

Clark and two men jumped into a skiff and rowed across the river, returning an hour later with the awaited pouch of letters.

Lewis laid aside the thick missive from his mother in favor of a thin envelope addressed in the familiar hand of President Jefferson. Reading it was a matter of moments.

"Captain Clark, may I have a word with you?"

The redheaded Clark, already deep in his own letters, grunted good-naturedly and followed Lewis into the tent.

"What ails you, Captain? You look positively pale."

"What I suspected has happened. Listen to this." Lewis read from the President's letter:

It is my pleasure to inform you that Mr. James Monroe
has recently returned from France. The Emperor Napoleon refused to sell New Orleans; insisted that we
buy the whole of Louisiana instead.

"The whole of Louisiana!" gasped Clark. Lewis read on:

This he negotiated for the sum of $11,250,000. Con-
sequently you will be traveling through American, instead of French, territory. As you will be aware, it is
now more urgent than ever that we find out what we
have bought and establish our claim to the Columbia
River and all the land it drains. I am reliably informed
that the British are intensifying their efforts in this
direction.

"Whoever would have thought this possible so soon?" Lewis
exclaimed.

"Napoleon must be desperate for money."

"No doubt, but more desperate to keep Britain from seizing
Louisiana. So he chooses to let us have it instead. Nothing like
being the lesser of two evils, Clark. Do you see what this means?
We own the whole country, clear across to the Pacific, if we can
make good our claim to the Columbia."

"And only you and I and our little army to do it," said Clark
soberly. "No wonder you look pale, Captain."

"And here are the President's final instructions." Lewis continued:

The object of your mission is to explore the Missouri
River & such principal stream of it, as, by it's course &
communication with the waters of the Pacific Ocean,
may offer the most direct & practicable water com-

munication across this continent, for the purposes of commerce.

Well, there it is. We start tomorrow."

To a person of our day, this statement of Jefferson's reveals clearly the errors in geographical knowledge prevailing at the opening of the nineteenth century. In spite of Alexander Mackenzie's demonstration that there was no Northwest Passage through Canada, the dream still persisted of a water crossing of the continent farther south.

Jefferson believed the headwaters of the Missouri and Columbia to be mingled or separated by only a short land traverse. In this belief, he had plenty of support. One explorer of the time reported that Indians told him there was a portage of only twenty miles between the two rivers. Another said there might be a ridge of hills between, but it would be passable by horse, foot or wagon.

Most felt sure of one thing; somehow there had to be a way to go by canoe through the Rocky Mountains. Nobody yet had any real idea of their size, height or extent. Had Lewis and Clark dreamed that instead of a twenty-mile portage, they would have two hundred and twenty miles of difficult travel from the source of the Missouri to the headwaters of the Columbia system, it might have been too much even for them to face.

All they knew when they set the sail on their keelboat next morning and headed up the Missouri was that their first goal was the so-called Mandan Villages, home of the Indian tribe of that name, sixteen hundred miles ahead, sixty miles from the present city of Bismarck, North Dakota. Traders had penetrated to this point but no farther. Here, Lewis determined to spend the winter of 1804–1805, to be ready when ice left the rivers the next spring to make the supposedly quick trip to the Pacific and back. He fully expected it could be accomplished in one season.

The first obstacle was the presence of hostile Indian tribes between St. Louis and his proposed winter camp. The most powerful and warlike of these were the Sioux, who had subdued all other tribes and now stood astride the Missouri, preying on all trade in either direction. Many were the tales of robbery, beatings and killings of traders who tried to resist them.

Lewis and Clark knew that somehow they must assert the dominance of the United States over this tribe and, if possible, without fighting them openly. Clark had had more experience than Lewis in dealing with Indians so the main duty of negotiation was left to him. As the expedition progressed, there were times when Lewis found himself alone in crises. In these instances, he proved that he, also, was an expert in this field.

Both captains had one quality that distinguished them from the other explorers except David Thompson; they liked Indians, respected them, and thought of them as human beings like themselves. In response, Indians liked them, especially Clark, whom they called Chief Redhead. This trait, plus a firm refusal to be frightened or blackmailed, accounts for the success with which they moved through Indian country. That this would be true, they did not know on this Fourteenth day of May, 1804, as the "jentle breeze" of Clark's description caught the sail of their keelboat and sent it ahead against the current of the great Missouri.

Lewis deputized Clark to manage the boatmen while he proceeded along the shore to a promised rendezvous up the river a few miles. There, as President Jefferson's representative, he was to witness the lowering of the flag of France and the raising of the Stars and Stripes in token of a change of sovereignty.

Riding one of the two horses they were taking along for use of their hunters, with his big Newfoundland dog, Scammon, trotting beside him, he had plenty of time to think about the great change in world affairs which had just taken place, which was to be called by history, the Louisiana Purchase. As yet, the area was almost unknown, even as to its boundaries. Nobody was aware that it more than doubled the size of the United States.

Through conversations with the President, Lewis knew that France had originally owned it by right of exploration; that she had ceded it to Spain some years before the American Revolution; then, Napoleon's coming to power had forced its return. Now, unexpectedly, it had fallen into the lap of the new republic.

Lewis wondered, as he rode, if Mr. Jefferson also was thinking how much hung upon the outcome of this expedition and that it was a heavy responsibility he had given to a man only twenty-nine years old. Clark was thirty-three, but Lewis recognized that his own was the position of leadership.

Clark, the better riverman, continued to command the boats while Lewis walked along the shore or tramped inland, making observations of the land and animals and taking specimens of plants which he carefully mounted to send back to President Jefferson.

Drewyer, the most expert hunter, and from two to five others, constantly ranged the country on both sides of the river, to supply the large quantity of meat needed for so many men.

Both captains kept a careful, detailed journal of each day's events, and encouraged the men to do likewise. Several of them did so, though not with the wealth of scientific detail included in the captains' journals. Among those that have come down to us are the accounts by Sergeants Gass, Ordway and Floyd, the latter brief because of Floyd's early death.

The party arrived at the mouth of the Platte River on Saturday, July 21. Clark estimated they had come six hundred miles, a variation of only eleven miles from the correct distance. Here they found difficulty in passing the sand bars at the mouth, the current of the Platte being very powerful, running through many channels, none of them more than five or six feet deep.

Across the river and a few miles upstream, the expedition made camp and called neighboring Indian tribes to a council near the present Council Bluffs. President Jefferson had recommended such meetings and recognition of the leaders by means of certificates. These were printed forms which Lewis carefully made out to the principal chiefs as evidence of their superior position. Accompanied by an appropriate gift, varying from a red coat, cocked hat trimmed with feathers, an American flag or a medal for the most important chiefs, to trinkets of brass, mirrors and buttons for lesser ones, a certificate proved a man's standing.

One surly chief scornfully returned his certificate, demanding a better present. When Lewis refused to give it, the chief thought better of his actions and asked to have the certificate returned. Lewis, with the dignity he so well knew how to assume, reminded the chief that he had spit upon his Great White Father and could expect no further favors. This action enhanced the value of the certificates and, though only pieces of paper, they were eagerly sought by other Indian tribes.

This first council was successful in setting up friendly relations with the Otoes and Pawnees. The more warlike Sioux were still ahead.

Both captains in their notes speak of the beauty of the country. Under date of July 30, Clark writes:

> This prairie is covered with grass of ten or twelve inches in height, soil of good quality and at the distance of about a mile still further back, the country rises about eighty or ninety feet higher and is one continued plain as far as can be seen. From the bluff on the second rise

immediately above our camp, the most beautiful prospect of the river up and down and the country opposite presented itself which I ever beheld. The river meandering the open and beautiful plains, interspersed with groves of timber and each point covered with tall timber, such as willow, cottonwood, mulberry, elm, sycamore, linden and ash.

Early in August, they arranged a second council, for the chiefs of the Omaha tribe, sending with their invitation some roast meat and meal. In return, the Indians sent a gift of watermelons which was most welcome. The captains entertained their guests by showing them their air gun, parading the men, and having York, Clark's Negro servant, who was a born comedian, dance for them. This council, like the first, went off well.

As related by Lewis and Clark, the trip thus far sounds easy and smooth. They rarely mention the fact that the men are wrestling daily with the problems of sand bars and snags, of caving banks, and the roily water in which they must constantly spend hours and days. Perhaps this had something to do with an outbreak of skin troubles, carbuncles and boils. All these difficulties were only the common and expected accompaniment of this sort of life and seem to have received little attention.

An exception was the illness of Sergeant Charles Floyd, a likable young man whose symptoms worried the captains since they knew nothing to do for him. Their comments indicate that he suffered from an inflamed appendix which finally ruptured, causing his death. It was a blow to the morale of the whole party and when they buried the sergeant, near the present site of Sioux City, Iowa, no doubt many wondered if they also would die before the journey's end.

The same thought must have been in their minds every time someone ate a strange plant or fruit or drank water which made him ill, a condition which happened fairly often.

On August 23, one of the hunters killed a buffalo, the first one the expedition had seen. From this time on, buffalo meat was to be one of their staple foods. The heat through the Missouri Valley at this time of year was most oppressive. The men were tormented by ticks and mosquitoes and buffeted by violent thunder storms. Even the dog Scammon suffered a heat stroke one day and the men had to carry him to a creek where he could cool off.

Then, on August 27, young George Shannon failed to return from a hunting trip. Lewis did not worry for a day or two but when a week had gone by with no sight of him, he recalled that Shannon was not much of a hunter. Out there in the wilderness he could be dying of hunger and thirst.

He sent an expert hunter, John Colter, to look for him but he returned after several days with nothing to report. Sadly, Lewis reflected that the boy was probably dead, either from hunger or Indian attack. Perhaps, though he did not write it in his journal, he even blamed himself for accepting so young a recruit.

On September 11, fifteen days after the boy's disappearance, the men heard a shout and from up ahead of them, a bedraggled figure approached.

"Shannon!" The cry went up from half a dozen throats. George limped into camp. Lewis looked at him sternly.

"Where have you been? You have caused us much anxiety."

"I'm sorry, sir. I thought the boats had passed ahead of me. I've been trying for two weeks to catch up. Then, today, at a bend up yonder, I looked back and saw the sail of the keelboat."

"So all this time you have really been ahead of us."

"Yes, sir."

The men slapped him on the back, the only way they could tell him their joy that he was again with them.

Past the mouth of the James River, the Niobrara and the White, they sailed the big boat. The plain was so velvety emerald that Lewis noted, "it looks like a bowling green in fine order." Another thing that impressed him was his first sight of antelopes running, saying it was "more like the flight of birds than the motion of quadrupeds."

In mid-September, they came to the so-called "grand detour" of the Missouri, where the boats had to travel thirty miles around a neck of land only two thousand yards across. Here they had one of their narrow escapes, which Clark describes under date of September 21:

> At half past one o'clock this morning the sand bar on which we camped began to undermine and give way, which alarmed the sergeant on guard. The motion of the boat awakened me; I got up and by the light of the moon observed that the sand had given away both above and below our camp and was falling in fast. I ordered all hands on as quick as possible and pushed off. We had pushed off but a few minutes before the bank under which the boat and pirogues lay gave way, which would certainly have sunk both pirogues. By the time we made the opposite shore our camp fell in. We made a second camp for the remainder of the night and at daylight proceeded on to the gouge of this great bend and breakfast.

The first crucial days of the trip were at hand. They were approaching the country of the Sioux. Lewis chose for the council place a sand bar in the mouth of the Teton River, about midway through the present state of South Dakota. Here the men raised a flag-staff and made an awning of cottonwood branches for shade. The chiefs and their followers assembled at noon and after the usual custom of smoking a peace pipe, Lewis made a speech describing the purpose of their mission and detailing the new position of the United States.

Then came the ceremony of giving presents to the five principal chiefs. To Black Buffalo, the leader, went a red coat, cocked hat and feather; to others, medals, an American flag, some knives and bright silk handkerchiefs; to all, tobacco. The chiefs complained that these presents were not enough. They demanded one of the pirogues and all its contents, else the party would not be allowed to proceed up the Missouri.

They had played this game with white traders many times before. At a signal several hundred warriors appeared along the banks above the sand bar, their bows strung and arrows ready to fly. The rules of the game prescribed that upon seeing they were so badly outnumbered, the white men would give in.

Always before, the plan had worked but this group of men was different. Instead of dropping their weapons and surrendering, every man raised his rifle, finger on trigger, while Clark jumped to the howitzer mounted at the stern of the boat and swung it toward the bank, shouting an order that the women and children should get out of the way.

The jig was up. The Indians did not want to fight when they would have to pay a heavy price from their own warriors. Their arrows went back into the quivers and the braves slunk away. For two more days they hung around the camp, alternately threatening and whining of their poverty but the fight had gone out of them. Even in this situation, however, the captains did not forget the dignity of the chiefs but by feasting, taking some of them on the boat at intervals, and giving them presents and certificates, helped them save face with their own people.

Several weeks later, when the Americans came to the country of the Aricaras, or Rees, as they were generally called, the word had evidently reached them of the new sort of white men coming up the river. The chiefs received the travelers very cordially and said the road before them was open and no one dared close it. They could depart at their pleasure.

On October 25, the party arrived at the Mandan Villages, and barely in time, too, since snow had already appeared. They set up camp and began to build their fort which they completed in a month.

Named Fort Mandan, it was situated on a point of low ground on the north side of the Missouri covered with tall old cottonwood trees. The buildings consisted of two rows of huts joined at an angle to make a triangle with the front open. Each row consisted of four rooms, fourteen feet square and seven feet high, with plank ceiling and slanting roof which formed a loft above the rooms. Across the open side of the triangle they erected picketing and in the angle, built two rooms for stores and provisions.

The party soon had visitors. One was a dirty, slouching Frenchman named Toussaint Charbonneau who represented himself as an interpreter. With him were his two wives, one a mere girl.

Lewis and Clark did not like the looks of this man but they did need an interpreter who had a knowledge of the dialects spoken by westward tribes, especially the Snake Indians or Shoshones, who would be either their best friends or worst enemies.

"Can you speak the Snake tongue?" Lewis asked the shifty-eyed trader.

Charbonneau shrugged, then twitched a thumb toward the girl. "Shoshone woman."

Lewis pricked up his ears. The girl was very young but she was clean and tidy compared to the other squaws hanging around the camp and her black eyes looked into his with quick intelligence. Lewis knew it would not do to let the Frenchman guess he was employing him because of his wife, so he talked further with him, then told the fellow he would take him along, providing his young wife went, also.

Charbonneau shook his head. "Have papoose soon. Leave here."

This information somewhat staggered the two captains. Could they take along a woman with a young baby?

"But we have to have someone who understands the Snake language," Lewis argued.

Charbonneau thought he saw an advantage and said he would not go. Not enough money offered.

"All right," Lewis said and walked away.

A day or two later, the Frenchman came meekly to his tent and confessed to having been drunk when he had refused the captain's offer. Please to accept his humble apologies. He wanted nothing more than to go with the white men and tell them truly what the wretched Snakes, with their crooked tongues, said.

"The woman goes, too," Lewis insisted.

"Of course. She my best wife. Leave other here."

Once again, the captains had shown their ability to see through a bluff.

A second visitor was not so easily handled. Accompanied by several voyageurs, he came to the post one winter day, a fur trader named François Larocque. The captains received him courteously as they did all visitors, invited him to dinner and gave him and his men sleeping room.

When they had retired to their own quarters for the night, Clark said, "I've found out who this fellow is. One of the Indians told me. He is the man who has been giving medals and flags to our Indian friends and telling them their Great White Father is King George of England."

"A Nor'wester," Lewis guessed. "One of Mackenzie's men."

The next day, Larocque requested an audience and asked, with deceptive humility, to be a member of the captains' expedition.

Blandly, Lewis said no, then his tone stiffened. "Furthermore, you are trespassing on the soil of the United States. You may trade here but you will give no more presents to Indians living below the forty-ninth parallel."

Larocque withdrew and soon started back north with his retinue of canoemen. Before they left, one told an American that Larocque was going back to his headquarters in the North for further instructions.

Lewis then called a conference with some of the chiefs who had been receiving Larocque's gifts. "Larocque has been speaking to you with a double tongue," he told them. "He tells you what is not true. Your Great White Father lives in Washington, D.C. He will bring you trading posts here near your own homes and help you grow rich. If you take any more gifts from the King George men, he will be angry and cast you off." With this warning, reinforced by fine red arm bands and silk handkerchiefs, he sent them to pass the word to their people.

The weather turned very cold but the men were comfortable, well fed, and happy. Often they enjoyed dancing to the music of Cruzatte's fiddle. The dances were the square figures of the frontier and half the men wore arm bands to designate them as taking the part of ladies.

They celebrated New Year's Day, 1805, with a noisy party though the temperature hovered around forty degrees below zero. A few days later, Indians of the nearby village set out to search for a man and boy who had not returned from a hunting party. About mid-morning, they brought in the boy, thirteen years old, his feet frozen from spending the night in the open; no fire, and only a buffalo robe to cover him. His clothing consisted of a pair of leggings made of thin antelope skin and moccasins. The older man, though wearing even less, had not suffered any injury.

The captains put the boy's feet in cold water and he recovered except for the loss of two or three toes. Constantly, in their journals, they recorded their amazement at the ability of the Indians to endure cold.

Throughout this winter, unusually severe even by North Dakota standards, the men hunted, sawed firewood, made dugout canoes and occasionally frolicked. Meat was plentiful to the point where they became very choosy, eating only the best parts of the animal and throwing the rest away.

Lewis spent his time interviewing every Indian he could corner, to learn about the rivers and mountains of the West, as well as the nature of the tribes they would meet. Carefully, he and Clark put together these bits of information until they had compiled a fairly accurate forecast of their trip. Clark drew a map of the upper Missouri which carried in detail the streams entering from both north and south, so they already knew by hearsay almost every river they later encountered.

They were specially interested in Charbonneau's young wife and her tribe, the Shoshones, part of the Snake nation. Five years before, when the girl was only twelve years old, she had been kidnapped in a raid on her tribe. Charbonneau had won her from her previous master in a gambling game. Her name was Sacajawea, meaning Bird Woman.

On February 11, she gave birth to her first child, a fine boy who was named Baptiste, soon nicknamed Pompey or Pomp. He became the pet of the whole camp, especially of Captain Clark.

Early in March, the trader Larocque returned from his trip to headquarters with important news. Simon McTavish, for years the unquestioned head of the North West Company, had died, ending the long feud between him and Alexander Mackenzie. Now the Nor'westers had merged with Mackenzie's opposition company and were planning to send explorers into the West.

The captains knew they had no time to lose. Lewis packed up his reports and the specimens of plant and animal life he wished to send to the President and the extra men set off in the keelboat for St. Louis.

3

THAT same day, April 7, 1805, the two captains and their stripped-down crew started up the Missouri on what they expected would be a journey of a few months only, that would bring them back to this camp by the next winter. As usual, Clark commanded the boats, now reduced to the two pirogues and six small canoes, while Lewis walked along the shore, Scammon trotting beside him.

He was something of a philosopher and when action had been thick and fast for a while, he liked to go off by himself to think over what he had done and was about to do. That night, he recorded his feelings:

> Our vessels consisted of six small canoes and two large pirogues. This little fleet, altho' not quite so respectable as those of Columbus or Capt. Cook, were still viewed by us with as much pleasure as those deservedly famed adventurers ever beheld theirs; and I dare say with quite as much anxiety for their safety and preservation. We were now about to penetrate a country at least two thousand miles in width, on which the foot of civilized man had never trodden . . . and these little vessels

contained every article by which we were to expect to subsist or defend ourselves. However . . . entertaining as I do the most confident hope of succeeding in a voyage which had formed a darling project of mine for the last ten years, I could not but esteem this moment of my departure as among the most happy of my life.

Out of his original party, he had chosen with great care the men for the final dash. Most of them, after this journey, did nothing remarkable but for their part in this enterprise they deserve to be remembered by name.

Besides the two captains, Meriwether Lewis and William Clark, there were three sergeants, Nathaniel Pryor, John Ordway and Patrick Gass; Privates William Bratton, John Colter, Joseph and Reuben Fields, John Shields, George Gibson, George Shannon, John Potts, John Collins, Joseph Whitehouse, Richard Windsor, Alexander Willard, Hugh Hall, Silas Goodrich, Robert Frazier, Peter Cruzatte, Baptiste Lepage, Francis Labiche, Hugh McNeal, William Warner, Thomas P. Howard, Peter Wiser and John B. Thompson; Clark's Negro servant York; George Drewyer, the best hunter of the lot, and also a good interpreter; Toussaint Charbonneau and his wife Sacajawea, both to serve as interpreters for the Snake Indians; one Mandan Indian and fat little Pompey, now two months old, who rode in his papoose cradle on his mother's back; and, of course, Scammon.

Before the first day was over, Sacajawea proved her usefulness by showing the white men unknown sources of food. When they halted for dinner, she took a sharp stick and poked around some small heaps of driftwood until she opened caches of wild artichokes which mice had collected and hoarded. These the men found delicious.

This action was characteristic of Sacajawea throughout the trip. She not only endured all the hardships of the men but, in addition, cooked for her fretful husband and cared for her baby. Always, she used her Indian lore any way she could to be helpful.

Little Pompey, also, comes in for his share of praise. No soft crib for this Indian baby. From morning to night he was strapped to his cradle board, his legs held firmly by bindings of deerskin. No clean diapers and frequent changes to keep him comfortable, only dry moss packed about his little body and changed whenever the canoes stopped long enough to give his mother a chance. Every night Sacajawea released his bindings, washed and fed him and let him kick for a while before drawing him under her blanket to sleep. All day he rode on her back, his little head bobbing against her shoulder.

The two were a humanizing influence in that rough crew. Sacajawea won the respect and admiration of every man among them and the baby became a universal pet. Especially was Captain Clark taken with him. He called him, "My boy, Pomp," and saw to it that Charbonneau did not mistreat either him or his mother.

At first, the fleet made good time. Buffalo in large numbers grazed the plains, also elk, deer and antelope. Food was plentiful and easy of procurement. Even Scammon had become a good hunter, his method being to watch for animals swimming in the river, jump in and drag them down.

On April 26, the party reached the mouth of the Yellowstone River. Lewis sent a man up the stream with orders to examine it as far as he could and still return the same evening. He himself carefully studied the country around the mouth, noting the topography, the trees, soil and general situation as a possible site for a trading post. Clark's job was to measure the width and depth of the water, likewise with an eye to the commerce they expected soon to see crossing the continent by canoe. Clark also talked with the Indians about the source of this stream and they mistakenly informed him it was navigable nearly to its source in the Rocky Mountains, and at this point would be adjacent to a branch of the Columbia.

Along in May, they saw their first grizzly bear. The Indians had been telling of this fearsome animal but the white men scoffed away their fears. They had seen plenty of bears themselves. When, however, ten shots were required to kill the animal, the men began to change their minds. In this part of their journey, grizzlies were plentiful and narrow escapes many. Lewis himself was spared a mauling, if not death, only by plunging into the river and gaining the shelter of a small island.

On another occasion, six hunters went out to attack a grizzly, four firing at almost the same time, each putting a bullet through him. Seemingly not even checked, the bear ran at them with open mouth, whereupon the other two fired, but the monster kept coming so furiously none had time to reload. Almost overcome, they reached the river and two jumped into a canoe; two others plunged over a twenty-foot bank into the stream. So enraged was the bear that he went right in after them and they were saved only when the two men still on shore, who had been able to reload, shot him through the head.

After a few such episodes, Lewis forbade any man to hunt alone and all used the utmost caution when dealing with grizzlies.

On May 14, with terrifying suddenness, the whole expedition came near ending in disaster. It was after sunset of a very warm day. The westering sun had become so blinding that the men had rigged a sort of screen or awning along the side of the boat, perhaps a strip of oilcloth upheld by two paddles, to give them a little relief. Charbonneau was at the helm of the white pirogue instead of Drewyer, who usually steered her. This was the largest and safest boat in their fleet but, as Lewis tells in his journal:

Charbonneau cannot swim and is perhaps the most timid waterman in the world; perhaps it was equally unlucky that Captain Clark and myself were both on shore at that moment, a circumstance which rarely happened; and though we were on the shore opposite to the pirogue, were too far distant to be heard or to do more than remain spectators of her fate.

In this pirogue were embarked our papers, instruments, books, medicines, a great part of our merchandise and in short almost every article indispensably necessary to . . . the enterprise in which we are now launched to the distance of 2200 miles . . . The pirogue was under sail when a sudden squall of wind struck her obliquely and turned her considerably. The steersman, alarmed, instead of putting her before the wind, luffed her up into it. The wind was so violent that it drew the brace of the squaresail out of the hand of the man who was attending it, and instantly upset the pirogue and would have turned her completely topsy-turvy, had it not been for the resistance made by the awning against the water . . . Captain Clark and myself both fired our guns to attract the attention if possible of the crew and ordered the halyards to be cut and the sail hauled in, but they did not hear us. Such was their confusion and consternation at this moment, that they suffered the pirogue to lie on her side for half a minute before they took the sail in. The pirogue then righted but had filled within an inch of the gunwales.

Charbonneau still crying to his god for mercy, had not yet recollected the rudder, nor could the repeated orders of the bowsman, Cruzatte, bring him to his recollection until he threatened to shoot him instantly if he did not take hold of the rudder and do his duty. The waves were running very high, but the fortitude, resolution and good conduct of Cruzatte saved her. He ordered two of the men to throw out the water with some kettles that fortunately were convenient, while himself and two others rowed her ashore, where she arrived scarcely above the water. We now took every article out of her and lay them to drain as well as we could for the evening, baled out the canoe and secured her.

Lewis goes on to relate that his own reaction had been to jump into the river and try to swim to the pirogue, knowing that there were two other men on board who could not swim. Fortunately, he realized in time the folly of his idea, since the pirogue was three hundred yards away and the waves so high a boat could hardly live, to say nothing of a man.

There was a hundred to one but what I should have paid the forfeit of my life for the madness of my project, but this had the pirogue been lost, I should have valued but little.

Two days later, Lewis is able to appraise the accident more objectively, finding that things are not as bad as they seemed:

By four o'clock in the evening, our instruments, medicine, merchandise, etc., were perfectly dried, repacked and put on board the pirogue. The loss we sustained was not so great as we had at first apprehended; our medicine sustained the greatest injury, several articles of which were entirely spoiled and many others considerably injured. The balance of our losses consisted of some garden seeds, a small quantity of gunpowder, and a few culinary articles which fell overboard and sunk. The Indian woman to whom I ascribe equal fortitude and resolution with any person on board at the time of the accident, caught and preserved most of the light articles which were washed overboard.

Once more, Sacajawea had proved herself an asset to the expedition.

Amid dangers from rattlesnakes and grizzly bears, the breaking of the towline on several occasions, fevers, digestive upsets, one man falling in such a way as to throw a shoulder out of joint, another slashing himself with his axe, and the constant battle with storms, both cold weather and intense heat, the party struggled on up the Missouri.

On May 29 they came to a river which Lewis named the Bighorn. Clark reconnoitered many miles up this stream and decided it should have a prettier name. He christened it Judith's River, in honor of Miss Julia Hancock of Fincastle, Virginia, a young lady only thirteen years old at the time, whose friends called her Judy. A flattering gift, this, for the girl who was later to become the captain's wife.

On June 3, the party arrived at the forks of the Missouri where two streams of seemingly equal size came together, one from the north and the other from the south. Which was the true Missouri?

Up to this point, the journey had proceeded on schedule and Lewis still expected to reach the Pacific and come back before winter. To do this, however, he could not risk traveling many days up the wrong stream. With his usual carefulness, he took time to study the situation. Choosing some of his most capable men, he sent small parties up both forks to study the color of the water, nature of the stream bed and the apparent direction from which the river came, thus to determine the probability that it would lead them toward the headwaters of the Columbia.

The returning explorers seemed to think the northern fork was the main river but still the captains were not sure. So the two of them set out alone, Clark on the southern fork and Lewis, the northern. After a few days, Lewis himself decided this was not the main stream, seeming to head too far in the north. He therefore named it Maria's River, for his cousin, Miss Maria Wood of Virginia. Half apologetically, he comments:

> It is true that the hue of the waters of this turbulent and troubled stream but illy comport with the pure celestial virtues and amiable qualifications of that lovely fair one; but on the other hand, it is a noble river.

In referring to the color of the stream, Lewis had in mind the peculiar whiteness of the water, "about the color of a cup of tea with the admixture of a tablespoonful of milk." For this reason, it also was called the Milk River. The Minnetares had a less complimentary name, "the river which scolds at all others."

Lewis accepted Clark's decision that the southern fork was the right one to follow, only one of the many occasions when Clark seemed to have an instinctive understanding of the geography of the West. His judgment was verified a few days later when Lewis, hunting ahead of the main party, heard the noise of falling water and knew he must be approaching the Great Falls of the Missouri, one of the landmarks Indians had reported.

On June 14, he was far enough ahead to find that there were actually five falls within an eighteen-mile stretch of the river, lowering its bed four hundred feet. The problem now was how to take boats around them since Lewis was still confident that he could continue by canoe all the way to the Pacific Ocean.

One thing was sure; the pirogues were too large for portaging.

They were therefore carefully hidden in brush on an island and the party undertook to take their six canoes around the falls. Since they were too heavy to be carried, like birchbark canoes, the captains came up with the scheme of making rough carriages with wheels, the forerunner of today's boat trailers, on which to mount them. Writes Lewis:

> We were fortunate enough to find one cottonwood tree . . . large enough to make our carriage wheels, about twenty-two inches in diameter; fortunate I say because I do not believe that we could find another of the same size perfectly sound within twenty miles of us.

From this tree they cut four sets of wheels, with couplings, tongues and traces to hold the canoes. They cut up the mast of the white pirogue for axle-trees. Then, for three terrible weeks, from June 21 to July 15, they pushed and pulled, carried and dragged the canoes and baggage the eighteen miles around the falls.

It was not steady, uphill climbing, but broken by frequent gullies when they had to tie draglines on their vehicles to keep them from smashing downhill, then push up the other side to regain the height they had lost. It was, the captain recorded, the most strenuous labor they had yet performed, made more difficult and painful by the prickly cactus that covered the ground. Though they reinforced the soles of their moccasins with buffalo rawhide, it would not turn the cactus thorns and every man had terribly sore feet.

Another near-tragedy came when a cloudburst caught Clark and his servant York, Charbonneau and Sacajawea, or Janey as they usually called her, one day when they were walking on shore. They sought shelter from what they expected would be only a heavy rain, in a deep ravine where Clark had seen shelving rocks that would protect them. Janey took her baby from his wrappings and all were enjoying the rest when Clark saw a wall of water sweeping down the ravine toward them, tearing everything from its sides.

"Cloudburst! Run!" he yelled. He grabbed his gun in one hand and with the other pushed Sacajawea with Pompey in her arms ahead of him up the hill. Charbonneau, as usual, was so petrified by fright that he could hardly move, in spite of Clark's constant yelling, "Hurry!"

At length, all scrambled to the top of the hill and, looking down, saw a torrent fifteen feet deep where they had been standing only a few moments before. Clark had lost his compass, shot pouch and horn, with powder and ball, and his moccasins. He later found the compass, but everything else was gone, including poor little Pompey's cradleboard and clothes, but at least they were all alive.

Now came another stretch of bitter labor, dragging the canoes inch by inch up a dwindling river until, on July 25, they reached the three forks of the Missouri, which they named the Jefferson, the Madison and the Gallatin, in honor of the President, the Secretary of State and the Secretary of the Treasury. They continued to follow the largest, or Jefferson, which Lewis believed must lead them closest to the source of the Columbia.

The mountains seemed strangely empty of life. Game was so scarce, the men were starving but, as Lewis writes,

> If any Indians can subsist in the form of a nation in these mountains with the means they have of acquiring food, we also can subsist.

If the men had any time or energy to consider the nature of the country through which they were now traveling, they must have noticed that they had left behind the horizontal landscapes they had so much enjoyed all the way up the Missouri—broad prairies, a sky like a great blue bowl coming down on all sides to touch the wide country. Even the trees, maples, cottonwoods, elms and birches spread their branches like huge umbrellas for shade and protection.

Here they had come to a perpendicular country—jagged peaks and cliffs that rose sheer from deep canyons to tear the sky into wispy shreds. Even the trees, firs, pines, spruces and tamaracks, were pointed and their needles sharp and bristly, repelling anyone who came near. This was a country which later travelers would describe with the comment, "You can't see the scenery; the mountains keep getting in the way."

Life was becoming more difficult in other ways, also. Whitehouse had injured one leg badly when a canoe upset and hit him, Clark had a terrific boil on one ankle, and all the men were weak from hunger. To make it even worse, young George Shannon was lost again for several days. Sounding the trumpet and firing signal guns did not bring his return. Hunters were dispatched to look for him but without success. Not until the ninth of August did the boy re-appear, having followed the wrong river for many miles and been forced to backtrack to find the party.

With their fortunes at the lowest ebb of the trip so far, suddenly Sacajawea began to recognize landmarks, especially a mountain she said her nation called the Beaver's Head, from a fancied resemblance to the head of that animal. This meant they were near the present Lemhi Pass, so Lewis set off with a small party to find the Shoshones or any other Indians who might have horses they could buy to carry their baggage. By this time, he had been forced to the painful knowledge that he could not penetrate the mountains any farther in canoes, nor could he make it to the ocean and back this year.

On the morning of August 11, he and McNeal were walking

together while Drewyer and Shields marched at some distance on each side, all searching for a road or trail. Suddenly, about two miles away, Lewis saw an Indian on horseback. With his field glass, he observed that the man's clothing differed from that of other Indians they had seen. Therefore, he must be a Shoshone. He was riding an "elegant horse," and carrying a bow and quiver of arrows.

Here was the big opportunity they had been hoping for. When he and the Indian were about a mile apart, Lewis took his blanket from his pack and made the signal of friendship known to all western tribes. Holding the blanket by two corners, he threw it in the air higher than his head, then brought it to earth as if spreading it to sit on, repeating the act three times.

He also signalled his men to stop. Drewyer did, but Shields did not see the signal. In vain did Lewis call the word *tab-ba-bone*, which meant white man, but the Indian, seeing Shields still approaching him, dashed off in fright. Terribly disappointed and angry at Shields, Lewis now tried to follow the track of the horse but rain made the trampled grass rise so the trail was soon lost.

Next morning, the four ate the last bit of venison in their packs and eventually came to a spring which Lewis recognized as the ultimate head of the Missouri River. That night he wrote:

> I had accomplished one of those great objects on which
> my mind has been unalterably fixed for many years.
> Judge then of the pleasure I felt in allaying my thirst
> with this pure and ice-cold water.

McNeal exhibited his joy by standing astride the little rivulet made by the spring and thanking God that he had lived to bestride the mighty Missouri. They continued over the divide and came to a spring on the west side of the mountain, from which issued a handsome creek of cold water, moving Lewis to write:

> Here I first tasted the water of the great Columbia River.

Before long, the four came around the side of a hill and there, close at hand, three Indian women sat on the ground. One ran away but the other two, seeing supposed enemies so close they could not hope to escape, sat with bowed heads as if reconciled to die. Lewis took the older woman by the hand and raised her up, as he repeated the word *tab-ba-bone* and pulled up his shirt sleeve to show her that his arm was white. His face and hands had been so constantly exposed to the sun that they were as dark as the Indians'. He gave the two some beads, awls and looking glasses. Also, he dabbed on their cheeks a little vermillion paint, to an Indian, woman's most desired beauty aid.

He informed them by signs that he wished to see their chiefs, so they set out together and after two miles, met a party of sixty warriors mounted on handsome horses which Lewis said in his journal would have done honor even to James River, Virginia. Lewis left his gun with his men and made them halt while he went ahead, carrying a flag.

Next came the long-drawn-out ceremonies so dear to Indian hearts, which drove Lewis to the verge of madness. The braves embraced him and rubbed their cheeks to his until, he says, "I was heartily tired of the national hug." Then all must sit down, take off their moccasins, a sign they intended to stay a while, smoke the peace pipe, receive gifts of blue beads and vermillion paint, and make speeches at great length before Lewis was allowed to explain the objects of his journey and his need of horses.

They seemed indifferent. As their chief, Cameahwait said, they were starving and interested in little but food. However, when Lewis described the man with the black skin and the Shoshone woman who belonged to his party, they reluctantly accompanied him. His hunters soon had the good luck to bring in several deer. These, the Indians tore up and ate raw, even to the entrails and hoofs, which so disgusted Lewis that he comments, "If I had not myself been starving, I could not have tasted that meat."

Then came a coincidence almost unbelievable. Captain Clark, walking up the creek in the hope of meeting Lewis, was accompanied by Charbonneau and Sacajawea. Suddenly he noticed her dancing and showing every sign of the most extravagant joy. She pointed to several Indians approaching on horseback and sucked her fingers to indicate they were of her native tribe.

> We soon drew near the camp [writes Clark] and just as we approached it a woman made her way through the crowd towards Sacajawea and recognizing each other, they embraced with the most tender affection. They had been companions in childhood, had both been taken prisoners in the same battle, they had shared and softened the rigours of their captivity, till one of them had escaped . . . with scarce a hope of ever seeing her friend relieved from the hands of her enemies.

But this was not all. When the white men and Indians sat down for a council, Sacajawea was brought in to interpret—the reason for her ever coming at all. As she sat down and began to speak, suddenly

> In the person of Cameahwait she recognized her brother. She instantly jumped up and ran and embraced him, throwing her blanket over him and weep-

ing profusely. The chief was himself moved, though not in the same degree . . . After the council was finished the unfortunate woman learnt that all her family were dead except two brothers, one of whom was absent, and a son of her eldest sister, a small boy, whom she immediately adopted.

Lewis learned that the Shoshone camp was on the headwaters of the Salmon River, now often called "The river of no return." He soon found it to be, as the Indians said, impossible of navigation. Not only that, but cliffs rose so sheer from the water that no one could even walk along the shore. However, they told him of another tribe, the Nez Percés, who lived some distance northward, on a stream which would take him to the ocean. It was a very bad trail, Cameahwait said, but once more Lewis decided that what Indians could do, white men could also accomplish.

At night, after the red men had gone to their camp, Lewis had his men dig a great cache for all the goods they could not carry with them. This they did by taking out a small piece of sod, eighteen inches in diameter, then hollowing out the ground below in the shape of a huge bottle, hiding the dirt in the woods. They lined the cache with branches and stowed their goods and baggage, replaced the circle of sod and built a fire over it, to conceal it with ashes. They also sank their canoes in a shallow pond.

Next day, they set out to find the Nez Percé trail which, Cameahwait said, led to the Kooskooske (Clearwater) and eventually to the Columbia. He had promised to stay with Lewis until he found this trail, but one morning Charbonneau mentioned casually that all the Indians would leave next day for the buffalo hunting grounds east of the Rockies. Sacajawea had told him, having been informed by her brother. Being only a woman and, in the eyes of the Indians, too inferior to speak directly to the white chiefs, she had used this method to relay the information to them. Charbonneau had been too indifferent or stupid to see the significance of the news and had waited until almost too late.

Clark had gone off to buy horses, so Lewis was alone and desperate. This was the greatest crisis of the journey and everything depended on his ability to touch just the right chord in the Indian mind. He called the chiefs together and asked if they were men of their word and if he could depend on their promises. When they assured him he could, he asked if they had not promised to help him cross the mountains. They agreed they had.

Very earnestly then, Lewis told them that without their help he could not get over the pass to the great river leading to the ocean and would have to return to his own country. In that case, no more white men would come, bringing trade goods and the guns and ammunition they needed to resist their enemies. He reminded them of his liberality in sharing the meat his hunters had brought in and urged them to keep their promise and countermand the order to go eastward.

Cameahwait, the head chief, remained silent for some time but finally admitted he had done wrong in deciding to leave, though all his people were hungry. He would cancel the order and carry out his promises.

Clark returned from his buying trip with twenty-nine horses and the party advanced along the Lemhi River to the main fork of the Salmon, then up the Bitterroot to a camp they named Travelers Rest. Soon they reached Lolo Pass and the main body of Indians left them. One old man, whom they called Toby, and his son, remained as guides.

Winter was coming on fast. Ice edged the creeks and frequent snowstorms blurred the trail. After an almost incredible struggle over hills and through ravines, with fallen timber and brush so thick they could hardly get through, they came, on September 14, to the head of Glade Creek, one of the sources of the Clearwater River. The slopes were so steep that several horses slipped and rolled down the sides, some so severely hurt they had to be destroyed. One such incident smashed Clark's small trunk and the writing desk he had carried thus far.

About the end of September, the party reached the Kooskooske or Clearwater, where once more they could use canoes. They branded their horses and left them in the care of Chief Twisted Hair of the Nez Percés, who promised to care for them until the next spring, and buried their saddles and a canister of balls. Food was very scarce, consisting almost entirely of dried fish and various roots which, after being eaten, bloated the men's stomachs so badly they could hardly breathe for several hours. Here, the guide Toby left them.

At last, however, they were on a navigable stream. They made new dugout canoes and on October 7, set out down the Clearwater. Three days later they reached the Snake, near the present city of Lewiston, Idaho. Here Clark's instinctive understanding of geography made him aware that this stream was part of the same system as the Salmon, where they had first hoped to descend the western slope of the Rockies.

The Snake brought them into the country of salmon eaters and very soon the men tired of a steady fish diet. They could find no more deer, so became accustomed to eating dog meat, as the Indians did. On October 16, they reached the confluence of the Snake with the Columbia and camped on the point now marked by Sacajawea Park, a few miles from the city of Pasco, Washington, the first white men to see the Columbia River east of the Cascade Mountains.

Lewis believed it to be the same river that Mackenzie had discovered twelve years earlier, a mistake that indirectly led to the expedition of Simon Fraser in 1808. Describing the country, Clark wrote:

> In every direction from the junction of these rivers, the country is one continued plain, low and rising from the water gradually, except a range of high country (now called the Horse Heaven hills) on the opposite side about two miles distant from the Columbia.

Surprisingly, the captains recorded in their journals very little of the exaltation they must have felt upon first viewing this river they had come so far to find. They wrote, rather, of the warm welcome given them by the local tribes of Indians. While Lewis attempted to learn something of their language, Clark and two men in one of the small canoes paddled upstream as far as the mouth of the Yakima River, where the city of Richland and the Hanford Atomic Works now stand.

Coming back, they stopped to buy dogs for food. They noted the large number of Indians who were partially or entirely blind, which they attributed to their constant fishing on such bright, glaring water, with no shade, and to the frequent severe storms of blowing sand and dust. Lewis prepared eye water, the drug he used not being mentioned, and gave it liberally to those with sore eyes. He soon acquired a reputation as a physician, which grew as he treated many for various diseases, using the simple remedies he had brought along.

More struggles with rapids and cascades, with occasional portaging around the worst places, brought the party in sight of the high, snow-covered peaks of Mt. Adams and Mt. Hood, and through the terrific chutes and falls about The Dalles. On November 1, they camped to prepare for descending the series of falls known as the Cascades, now the site of Bonneville Dam.

Here they had to carry all the luggage around the falls, using the men who could not swim and hence did not dare ride the canoes over the rapids.

Emerging successfully from the gorge of the Columbia, they began to see evidences of white men's visits to the Coast. They met Indians wearing caps, coats and woven blankets, and using kettles of brass and copper. Surrounded by fog, and soaked to the skin day in and day out by the perpetual rain, they were as miserable and uncomfortable as men could be.

At last, however, they were nearing the end of their journey. On November 7, 1805, Clark's entry in his journal was, "Ocian in view. Oh, the joy!" He was slightly mistaken, since they were still miles from the ocean proper but the ten-mile width of the lower Columbia deceived them. A week later they stood on the shore of the ocean and watched the breakers roll in over the bar that had hidden the river's mouth from so many early explorers.

They had reached their destination but before they could go home, they must wait out the winter and a dreary, soggy one it proved. For a while they camped on the north shore in the cold rain but finding no good location above high tide, they paddled across to the south bank and up a small tributary now called Lewis and Clark River. There, on a rise of land thirty feet above the water, they built two rows of tiny log huts facing each other across a twenty-foot parade ground and christened it Fort Clatsop, that being the name of the local Indian tribe.

Their fort has recently been rebuilt to Clark's dimensions, as the Fort Clatsop National Monument, four and one-half miles from Astoria, Oregon. Dwarfed by the huge fir and cedar trees around it, it still is a cozy little shelter as in the days when Lewis wrote, "All the party snugly fixed in their huts."

They had hoped a ship might come into the Columbia during

their stay, from which they might buy supplies and merchandise to trade on their homeward journey. Strangely, President Jefferson had overlooked sending one though he, like Lewis, expected the expedition to have returned by this time. One ship, but not of American registry, did enter the river and pass their camp site on the north shore, but they had already left it and in the fog did not see the ship.

Early in December, Captain Clark and five men cut a trail through the forest of huge pine, fir and cedar trees to the ocean. The fallen timber and swampy land were so difficult that Clark estimated the distance as seven miles instead of the actual three and one-half.

Christmas morning they celebrated with a salute, shouts and songs. Presents were distributed—tobacco for those who used it and for the others, bright handkerchiefs. Clark writes:

> I received a present of Captain Lewis of fleece hosiery, shirt, drawers and socks, a pair of moccasins of White-house, a small Indian basket of Goodrich and two dozen white weasel tails of the Indian woman.

For some time they had been without salt, so early in January several of the men set up a camp near Tillamook Head at the present site of Seaside, Oregon. Here they built a cairn or rock stove about eight feet long with a firebox open at one end to take the logs of cedar and fir and five holes in the top in which copper buckets were set to boil down sea water. During a two-month period they scraped four bushels of salt from the sides of these buckets. A replica of the cairn stands on the site today.

The most exciting event of the winter was a visit from a whale, thoroughly dead, that was washed up on the shore near Tillamook Head. A party went to see it. For the first and probably the only time of the whole expedition, Sacajawea summoned courage to put in a claim for what she felt she had earned—a chance to see the ocean and the great fish.

They took her along but by the time they reached the whale, all the flesh and blubber had been removed by the Indians, leaving only the skeleton, one hundred and five feet long. Lewis bought three hundred pounds of blubber and a few gallons of oil. After it had been boiled, the blubber tasted something like pork. Clark wrote:

> I thank providence for directing the whale to us; and think him much more kind to us than he was to Jonah, having sent this monster *to be swallowed by us,* instead of *swallowing of us* as Jonah's did.

Most of the journals of January, February and the first half of March say only, "No occurrence today worthy of note." To keep the men busy, the captains organized the camp like a military fort, held inspection on the parade ground, posted guards at the stockade gate and insisted on strict military discipline.

The captains wrote up their notes and drew maps; the men hunted and fished and fought the colds and rheumatism caused by the ever-present dampness and chill. They lived only for spring and the day they could start home. Lewis figured they could not cross the mountains until well into June, because of the deep snows, and estimated two months sufficient to take them from the ocean to their caches in the Rockies. On Sunday, March 23, 1806, they left Fort Clatsop.

Having heard of the famous lines left by Alexander Mackenzie on the rock at Bella Coola, Clark had done a bit of carving on a pine tree, "William Clark, December 3, 1805. By Land from the U. States in 1804 & 1805."

Lewis posted on the wall of the fort a brief report of the expedition and the names of those who took part in it. He gave

Courtesy, Canadian Government Travel Bureau

Modern view, Canyon of the Fraser River where the full volume of the river passes through a narrow gap called Hell's Gate.

Courtesy, Idaho Power Co. and th
Idaho Historical Societ

Canyon of the Snake River in southern Idaho, where Hunt's
party had to give up further travel by canoe.

*Photo by W. H. Jackson from the files of the
Idaho Historical Society*

Twin Falls on the Snake River in southern Idaho as they looked
in 1811.

Athabasca River, Alberta, Canada, was regularly used by early explorers and traders.

The Fraser River at its source just below Mt. Robson, 12,972 feet high, greatest elevation in the Canadian Rockies.

Columbia Lake, source of the Columbia River. Looking north toward the river's start on its 1200-mile journey to the sea.

Courtesy, British Columbia Dept. of Recreation and Conservation

As Thompson left Boat Encampment and once more paddled upstream, he had his first view of Mt. Trident, 10,141 feet high, in the Selkirk Range, which he christened Nelson.

Courtesy, British Columbia Dept. of Recreation
and Conservation

As Thompson completed the final portion of his exploration of
the Columbia River, he saw the mighty Selkirks but did not
explore Rogers Pass, which now affords a way through from
Revelstoke to Golden, B.C.

several copies to Indian friends. One copy later turned up in Philadelphia, having come by way of China on a trading ship.

The route home was much the same as on the westward journey though the party left the Columbia at the mouth of the Walla Walla River and went overland to the junction of the Snake and Clearwater Rivers, where the twin cities of Clarkston, Washington, and Lewiston, Idaho, now stand. Once more at Travelers Rest, near Lolo Pass, the expedition separated into two groups. Lewis and a few men took a direct route east to Great Falls, then up the Marias River. In the leader's mind was still that hope of Jefferson's that some stream entering from the north might offer a water route from the Saskatchewan so he turned aside to find out. Some distance up this stream, the party met eight Indians of one of the Blackfoot tribes. At first, they pretended to be friendly and all camped together. Lewis made the mistake of going to sleep that night, leaving only one man on watch. The Indians had sneaked away their guns and started to run off the horses when the white men awoke. They rushed their enemies and regained their guns but in the skirmish, one Indian was killed by stabbing and Lewis shot another.

Aware of their extreme danger, the Americans made a forced march back to the Missouri where some of the men were waiting. Grateful to have escaped, they hastened down the river.

Meanwhile Clark, with the main portion of the expedition, retraced the westward journey, retrieved the supplies from the great cache and raised the sunken canoes. During this journey, little Pompey, now almost eighteen months old, became very ill. Sacajawea called on all her Indian remedies but for a few days it seemed the baby might die and the whole camp was in mourning. At last he began to recover and the expedition continued.

Clark sent several men in the canoes down the Missouri to

meet Lewis at the mouth of the Marias. He and the others struck out fifty miles across country to the Yellowstone. Here, on a large rock which he named "Pompey's Pillar," he carved the date, July 25, 1806. Perhaps it was a token of joy over the baby's restored health.

At the mouth of the Yellowstone the two parts of the expedition were united again and went triumphantly back down the Missouri. Now that they were going with the current, the speed must have seemed phenomenal. In spite of that, this part of the trip occupied almost three months.

At the Minnetaree Villages on the upper Missouri, Charbonneau and his family left the party and soon John Colter, the hunter, likewise decided to stay in the West. There, the next year, he discovered Yellowstone Park.

On Tuesday, September 23, about noon, the little brigade reached St. Louis. They had been gone so much longer than expected that everyone had given them up for lost, but the good news spread fast. The whole city turned out to welcome them. A great dinner and ball were announced whereupon the two captains hastily took themselves to the tailor's to have suitable clothes made.

Too conscientious to spend much time in merry-making when they must report to President Jefferson, the captains cut the feasting short, paid off their crew and, with what must have been deep regret, said good-bye to the band of men who had stood by them so faithfully. The astounding fact was that after the death of Sergeant Floyd, not a man had been lost and even the dog Scammon returned in good health, proof of the skill with which the expedition had been organized and led.

Congress and the President gave each member of the party double pay for the twenty-eight months of the journey and five new uniforms. In addition, each enlisted man received three hundred and twenty acres of land and Lewis and Clark, fifteen hundred acres each.

That these tributes would be paid them they did not know when they bade one another farewell. Now Lewis and Clark must prepare their report for the President. On Friday, September 26, 1806, Clark made the final entry in his journal:

A fine morning. We commenced writing.

It would not have seemed so fine a morning had they known that only three years later, Lewis was to meet a violent death in a roadhouse in Tennessee where he had stopped for the night as he rode on horseback toward Washington. At the time, the verdict was suicide but many then and since have believed he was murdered, perhaps for money he was known to have been carrying.

William Clark became Governor of Missouri and sent for Pompey, or Baptiste, to live with him and go to school. For many years he worked to help the Indians whose problems he so well understood. He retained his health and vigor to old age and was greatly admired throughout his long life.

THE THIRD ROAD

Simon Fraser, 1808

I

THROUGHOUT the story of the five great expeditions across the country to the Pacific, one comes constantly upon evidences of the way they were inter-related; one explorer helping another without knowing it. As the Lewis and Clark expedition had received its impetus from President Jefferson's reading of Alexander Mackenzie's *Voyages* so, in turn, Lewis and Clark, without intending to, stimulated the next two explorations, those of Simon Fraser and David Thompson.

Fraser, like Mackenzie, was descended from an aristocratic Scottish family. His most famous relative, Baron Simon Fraser Lovat, had been a supporter of King James II and had been executed for his part in the plot to return the Stuarts to the throne of England.

Simon's father emigrated from Scotland in 1773 and the boy was born three years later in Bennington, Vermont, just as the American Revolution was getting under way. The father was a Loyalist and enlisted in the British forces, was captured and died in prison. His young widow brought her little boy to Canada, the refuge of many Loyalists, and he grew up in the town of St. Andrews. Again like Mackenzie, he received his education in Montreal and joined the North West Company at the age of sixteen. Evidently he proved his ability very soon, since he became a full partner at twenty-two.

Little is known of him during the next seven years, except that he was assigned to various posts in the far Northwest, on the Athabasca and Saskatchewan Rivers. He seems to have engaged in exploration only as it helped the fur trading business but he loved the wild western country and was constantly moving from one place to another. His name appears here and there in journals of other fur traders as having been seen at this or that place. Probably he would have lived and died unknown to history except for one thing: he was in the right place at the right time with the right training and experience for the work that was to be done.

This particular work was the search for the Columbia, the Great River of the West, Mackenzie's old dream, at long last included in the plans of the North West Company. To understand how the change came about, one must go back to Alexander Mackenzie and his return to England after quitting the company in 1799. When his famous book of travels was published and he had been knighted by the king for his achievements, there seemed nothing to prevent his settling down to enjoy the fruits of his work. He was only thirty-seven years old, wealthy, and could have anything he wanted.

Somehow, Canada still called him. Out there in the West, that great river of his dreams, now named the Columbia, still rolled, unexplored, to the sea. His self-appointed task was not yet finished; besides, he hated to acknowledge defeat at the hands of his enemy, Simon McTavish. So back to Montreal he came in the year 1802 and formed his own rival trading company with the purpose of making life as unpleasant as possible for McTavish. The fight was in the open and both loved a battle.

What a pity, then, that McTavish had to die in 1804, at the age of fifty-four.

At once, the affairs of the North West Company were in confusion. A great meeting of agents, partners and attorneys was called in Montreal. Mackenzie agreed to drop his rival company and come back into the North Westers' fold. Probably he expected to be elected their head, being the most experienced man among them. However, McTavish had two nephews, William and Duncan McGillivray, who also had served well. The upshot was that William was elected and Mackenzie became a sort of elder statesman.

He accepted the snub with good grace. All he wanted now was to get on with exploring the Columbia and securing its watershed for Great Britain. In this, he had the support of the younger McGillivray brother, Duncan. Through the years of his uncle's quarrel with Mackenzie, Duncan had been convinced that Alexander was right. He had even made an attempt himself to find the Columbia River.

Two or three years before, he had gone far up the Saskatchewan River to Rocky Mountain House, the farthest outpost of the company in the very foothills of the mountains. There he had secured the services of another young partner, David Thompson. Together they had set out to find the pass at the head of the Saskatchewan.

Thompson had never crossed this pass but through his Indian friends he knew it to be there. He soon discovered, however, that they did not want him to find it. They were Piegans, a division of the Blackfoot tribe, and feared that if traders once got over the mountains they would supply guns and ammunition to their enemies, the Kootenays and Flatheads.

They skilfully led the white men astray and left them stranded. The horses bogged down in snow and the men had to wade

continuously in icy streams. McGillivray developed severe rheumatism in his feet and legs and had to retreat to Rocky Mountain
House and spend the winter getting well. As soon as he could
hobble about on rough crutches, he left for the East, handing
over to Thompson the task of finding the Columbia. He himself
had had all he wanted of it.

In the winter of 1804, after the company meeting, McGillivray
and Mackenzie journeyed from Montreal to Fort William, on
Lake Superior, which had succeeded Grand Portage as the
central headquarters of the company. Here they met the trader
Larocque and learned the news of Lewis and Clark's expedition.
The Americans were on the march!

Mackenzie's years of persuasion now began to bear fruit. What
was to be done? What about David Thompson? He was supposed
to have explored the Columbia before this but no word had come
from him. The long-distance telephone of those days was the
birchbark canoe, gliding over rivers and lakes. Two months from
Fort William to Rocky Mountain House, two months back.
Duncan McGillivray could not wait either for that or to seek
council from his brother in Montreal—another two-month journey. He called in Larocque.

"You know the Missouri country, don't you?"

"*Oui*, M'sieur, I know heem."

"You get together a party and do some exploring yourself.
Draw on the company for supplies. What is the first big river
upstream from where the Americans are camped?"

"The Yellowstone, M'sieur."

"Does it head in the Rocky Mountains?"

The trader shrugged. "Who knows?"

"You go and find out. And keep watch of those Americans."

"*Oui*, M'sieur." Larocque licked his chops. A whole winter's
trading at company expense.

So during the long months of 1805 and 1806 while Lewis and Clark struggled over the mountains and down to the sea, Larocque and his small party traded happily along the Yellowstone, listening for news. In the spring he reported to McGillivray, "No reason to be disturbed about the Americans, M'sieur. Nothing has been heard of them. Likely the Indians have killed them all."

He was probably right, thought McGillivray. Otherwise that man Jefferson would have shouted to the world of their success. Old Uncle Simon was pretty smart, after all. Trading was the important thing.

Into this smug, comfortable situation, about the beginning of the year 1807, burst a bombshell in the form of the journal of Sergeant Patrick Gass, one of the Lewis and Clark party, first to get his record into print. The Americans had done it, after all!

Alexander Mackenzie scowled at the partners gathered in their annual meeting. "There is no time to lose. The Americans will soon own the whole Pacific Coast."

"What do you think we should do?" asked McGillivray.

"What we should have been doing the last ten years. Send men across the Rocky Mountains and build trading posts. Explore the Columbia to the sea."

"The Americans say they have discovered the Columbia headwaters in the Rocky Mountains below the forty-ninth parallel."

"They may have found one branch but the true Columbia is the one I discovered. I'm sure of it. All we have to do is finish what I began."

"Whom do we have who could lead such an expedition?"

"What about David Thompson?" suggested Mackenzie. "He is the most capable explorer and surveyor I've ever met."

"He may be," said Duncan, "but you remember he went with

me on that trip a few years ago. When I left, I told him to go on and explore the Columbia but we've heard nothing of it. What about Simon Fraser?"

"Fraser," mused Mackenzie. "Square, bushy-haired fellow with a face like a thunder cloud and a body like a rock?"

"That's Fraser. Start that rock rolling down the Columbia and nothing could stop it."

"Let's start it rolling. In fact, why not send both Thompson and Fraser? One or the other should succeed."

"If only Uncle Simon hadn't been so stubborn you would have done it before this, Sir Alexander."

Mackenzie smiled grimly. "Long before. And Great Britain would have owned the Columbia. Now we can only hope we are not too late."

2

SIMON FRASER relished the idea of exploring beyond the Rocky Mountains. As McGillivray knew, he was a restless, lonely man who never stayed long in any one place. He had not the imagination of Mackenzie and the dream of saving the Columbia for Great Britain seems not to have occurred to him. He was the fur trader, first and last. Any exploring he had done up to this time had been merely to open new fur country. In fact, he had already followed Mackenzie's old trail up the Peace River, during the summer of 1805. Once across the pass and on the Parsnip, he had explored it to its source in the lake Mackenzie found, named it McLeod for another partner and built a trading post there which he also named McLeod.

The next spring, another Nor'wester, John Stuart, appeared there. The two got along well together and continued explorations through the wild, jagged mountains of British Columbia.

Beneath their rough exterior, they were both sentimental Scots and this lovely, untamed country reminded them of their homeland. They named it New Caledonia, using the old Roman name for their beloved Scotland.

For a whole year they roamed its mountains and canyons, rivers and lakes, naming them for friends, as well as themselves. They set up a few more trading posts and even made friends with the fierce Carrier Indians, to whom they first introduced the charms of tobacco and soap.

In the spring of 1807, the messengers sent by McGillivray reached Fraser with his orders to go down the supposed Columbia to the sea. Fraser, welcoming a new adventure, began preparations at once, but he was too experienced a wilderness man to undertake such a mission without careful preparation.

He and Stuart established a supply base on the river we know as the Fraser, at the mouth of its tributary, the Nechako, and named it Fort George for the king. Here they began assembling supplies, which had to be brought in those familiar ninety-pound packages by canoe and portage clear from Montreal. The length of the supply line had now been extended to more than three thousand miles. A full year went by before they had gathered enough guns and ammunition, pemmican and jerked meat, and a crew of experienced canoemen.

In the spring of 1808, Fraser was ready. With Stuart as his second in command, nineteen voyageurs and two Indian guides, he set out on May 28 leading a fleet of four canoes on one of the most dangerous and difficult journeys undertaken by any explorer in the history of North America.

The Fraser is eight hundred and fifty miles long and in the course of its journey describes roughly the shape of the letter "S". Blocked at every turn by mountains, it twists and turns, whirls and spits, writhing like a wounded yellow snake. Only in its lower reaches can it be called smooth-flowing. Elsewhere it is a succession of rapids, falls and cataracts which have defied all attempts at navigation.

Fortunately Simon Fraser did not know when he started out how bad it was going to be but perhaps, even if he had known, he would have tried it anyhow. The impossible was a challenge to this stubborn, bushy-haired, rock of a man. Besides, he had been annoyed and perhaps a bit jealous at all the attention given Alexander Mackenzie at that Montreal conference a few years back. What was so great about Mackenzie? He had failed to conquer this river, hadn't he? So let Simon Fraser show who was the greater explorer.

It was the time of the spring run-off and the river rose rapidly, eight feet in twenty-four hours. The Indians, as timid as Mackenzie's guides had been, tried to back out of their agreement. One said his wife and children would starve while he was gone. Another frankly admitted he feared the rapids. Finally, Fraser insisted that one of them sleep in his own tent and spread the Indian's robe, alive with fleas, under his own. It probably was an uncomfortable night for Fraser but the guide was still there in the morning. Anyhow, sleep was difficult with the constant roar of the turbulent stream in their ears.

Within the first fifteen miles, trouble began. One canoe was damaged and almost lost in wild Fort George canyon. Two days later, the party passed the site of present Alexandria, the farthest point that Mackenzie had reached. Beyond this, all was new and unexplored. The men could see Indians watching from the shore and observed messengers dashing off on horseback, presumably to warn the tribes farther down of approaching danger.

This prompted Fraser to stop for a few days until a number of Indians could be brought together and he could explain his purpose. These were men of the Atnah tribe whose language Fraser did not understand. Among them, however, he found one slave boy who could speak the familiar Carrier dialect of New Caledonia.

Upon acquaintance, the Atnahs became friendly but warned Fraser that the river was one long succession of falls and cascades between impassable cliffs. They would be wise to go back before it was too late. Fraser was that rock set to roll down the supposed Columbia. At no matter what cost, he declared, he would go to the ocean. Who would guide him?

Reluctantly, the Indians admitted that in the next village, the chief had a slave who had journeyed to the sea. Perhaps he would be their guide. This tribe had never before seen white men or firearms and asked Fraser about the guns he and his men carried. When he ordered the men to fire at trees, the Indians fell on their faces in terror. These men were gods, and must be obeyed.

At the village below, the great chief himself volunteered to guide Fraser's party, saying he knew the tribes along the river and could guarantee peace. Fraser accepted this good fortune with the same imperturbability he showed in the face of danger. A few miles farther down the river, he began to understand what the Indians had meant by dangerous rapids and impassable cliffs. The channel narrowed to forty or fifty yards and the immense volume of the stream literally stood on edge. Cliffs rose sheer from the water so no one could even walk along the shore.

After surveying the impossible situation, Fraser picked his five best men to try to take one canoe through the rapids. For one moment only they could control her and got through the first cascade. Then the boat was drawn into an eddy and whirled about like a straw. The crew could do nothing more than keep her afloat. Round and round the whirlpool they raced, now sucked into the center, now flung out for a moment, escaping the rock walls by a hairbreadth.

Watching their chance, as the paper-thin boat was forced against a projecting rock, the men leaped out and managed to pull the canoe out of the water. How to save them? With unquestioning courage, a rescue party climbed along the face of the cliff, thrusting their daggers into the rock for handholds. Having reached the men and canoe, they fastened a line to her bow. Step by step, cutting hand- and foot-holds into the solid rock, some of the men struggled to the top, carrying the line. Others, bearing the canoe with her precious cargo of supplies on their shoulders, climbed up after them.

As they pushed and pulled their way up the cliff, the lives of all hung on that slender line and the care they used in placing each hand and foot. One false move and all would have plunged into the torrent below. Even when they had succeeded, their troubles had only begun. Everything they had must come up this same tortuous way. Somehow, they made it.

The Indians, standing by to watch, probably wondered how foolish the white men could be, anyhow. They told Fraser that if he would leave his canoes with them and go overland toward the rising sun he would come to another river which was much easier of navigation. Lower down, it emptied into this terrible Tacoutche Tesse and thus would lead him to the sea.

Not for nothing was Simon Fraser a Highlander, descendant of a Jacobite who had given his life for Bonnie Prince Charlie. Besides, he lacked imagination and had to depend on loyalty instead. He had been ordered to go down this river—no other, but this very Tacoutche—to the sea and down it he would go. To make clear his stand, he that night wrote in his journal:

> Going to sea by an indirect way was not the object of my undertaking. I therefore would not deviate.

Fraser was not as oblivious of the dangers as he pretended to his men. Following one specially trying day he wrote in his journal:

> This afternoon the rapids were very bad. Two in partic-
> ular were worse if possible than any we had met with,
> being a continual series of cascades intercepted with
> rocks and bounded by precipices and mountains that
> seemed at times to have no end. I scarcely saw anything
> so dreary and dangerous in any country and at present
> while writing this, whatever way I turn my eyes moun-
> tains upon mountains whose summits are crowned
> with eternal snow close the gloomy scene.

Begging some horses from the Indians, the men loaded their goods and walked along the rim of the canyon, so steep and dangerous that one horse fell over into the torrent, carrying Stuart's desk and the medicine chest.

When they once more got down to the river, they succeeded in navigating it for a few days, then came to another of the narrow canyons where the water seemed to be turned on edge. Above, the immense cliffs leaned toward each other as if looking down upon the foolish human beings who challenged them. Here, there was no possibility of climbing to the top, so, as Fraser records,

> The whole party, without hesitation and with most des-
> perate daring embarked in their canoes. Thus skimming
> along as fast as lightning, the crews, cool and deter-
> mined, followed each other in awful silence and, when
> we arrived at the end, we stood gazing at each other
> in silent congratulation at our narrow escape from total
> destruction.

At length even Fraser had to concede that they could go no

farther by canoe. They hauled the boats up on scaffolds and cached part of the supplies. The rest was made into packs, as heavy as the men could possibly carry. From this point on, they went on foot except where they could hire canoes for short stretches. The difficulties they encountered are best described in Fraser's own words:

> As for the road by land, we could scarcely make our way with even only our guns. I have been for a long period among the Rocky Mountains, but have never seen anything like this country. It is so wild that I cannot find words to describe our situation at times. We had to pass where no human being should venture; yet in those places there is a regular footpath impressed, or rather indented, upon the rocks by frequent travelling. Besides this, steps which are formed like a ladder or the shrouds of a ship, by poles hanging to one another and crossed at certain distances with twigs, the whole suspended from the top to the foot of immense precipices and fastened at both extremities to stones and trees, furnish a safe and convenient passage to the natives; but we, who had not had the advantages of their education and experience, were often in imminent danger when obliged to follow their example.

The Indians reported to Fraser that white men had recently passed down a large river to the east but he was unimpressed. He had enough to think about with his own troubles. Day after day, the dangers and difficulties mounted. Once a man carrying a heavy pack was caught among rocks in such a way that he could not move or unload himself. Fraser crawled on hands and knees to the spot and managed to cut the thongs and let the pack drop into the river. Two miles of this sort of travel wore a pair of moccasins off a man's feet. After that, the man had to go barefoot until night when he could make another pair.

Finally the Indian guides who had accompanied them so far determined to leave and Fraser let them go. As a token of appreciation he gave the chief a large silver brooch. The man seemed delighted, turned it over and over in his hands but did not know where to fasten it to his person. Finally he pinned it in his hair and appeared well pleased.

Repeatedly, the chiefs asked Fraser why he did not take good advice and go overland to the other river but still the stubborn Scot would not give in. On June 14, as the Indians had predicted, this other river joined the Tacoutche. Fraser named it for his friend David Thompson, a name it still bears. From this point on, again bearing out what the Indians had said, the Tacoutche was more peaceful. Fraser hired canoes and the men thankfully took to their paddles. They began to see natives who carried new copper kettles, guns and blankets, proof they had come from the seacoast.

On the nineteenth of the month, Fraser met the great chief of the Hacamaughs and was taken to their camp where he had to shake hands with all twelve hundred members of the tribe. A few days later, another tribe, the Achinrows, also received him with cordiality. These people had good houses made of planks three or four inches wide, each overlapping the next.

These were communal homes, one of them six hundred and forty feet by sixty feet, all under one roof. It was partitioned into separate family compartments with fire holes in the center and smoke holes above. The camp stood in a grove of huge cedar trees, thirty feet or more in circumference.

The Indians here were rather contemptuous of white men. One old chief announced that he had traveled to the sea and seen their "great canoes". They were very proud men, he said.

He got up, clapped his two hands upon his hips and strode about the place with an air of importance. "This is the way they go." Fraser and his men laughed. No doubt they recognized the likeness to some white men they knew themselves.

The chief promised to lend Fraser a canoe the next day but when morning came he changed his mind. If he thought he could play games with this white man he was mistaken. As Fraser tells it:

> I therefore took the canoe and had it carried to the water side; the chief got it carried back. We again laid hold of it, he still resisted and made me understand that he was not only the greatest of his nation but equal in force to the sun. However as we could not go on without the canoe, we persisted and at last gained our point. The chief and several of the tribe accompanied us.

Obviously, the expedition was nearing its goal. They engaged new canoes and on the last day of June once more embarked, enchanted by the sight of a great mountain (Mt. Baker) in the distance. They camped among gigantic cedar trees, a pleasant situation except for the clouds of mosquitoes. Seals swimming in the river entertained them. Next day, said a native, they would reach the sea.

But they never did. Next day, trouble once more raised a forbidding hand. The River Indians were at war with the Coast Indians. They told Fraser if he went to the sea, their enemies would kill his whole party. For Fraser's voyageurs this was the end. They refused to go on, but he was not to be stopped and set off alone. Two miles below the friendly village, the river divided into the many channels forming its delta. There, only a few miles away, almost in view, was the ocean he had come to find but night was at hand and he had nothing to eat.

He had to go back to his friends. As stubborn as he, they refused to give him even a mouthful of food if he still persisted in going among their enemies. He was so determined to reach the sea, nothing but hunger could have stopped him. His men, however, listened to the war drums of their enemies and sensed that danger was in the air. Determined, stubborn Scot that he was, Fraser knew himself defeated at last. Hurt and humiliated, he confided to his journal:

> I must acknowledge my great disappointment in not
> seeing the main ocean, having gone so near it as to be
> almost within view.

He did take an astronomical observation and found the latitude to be forty-nine degrees. This was the last and worst blow. This river could not be the Columbia, whose mouth was known to be at forty-six degrees, twenty minutes. One can hear the grief in Fraser's comment,

> If I had been convinced of this when I left my canoes,
> I would certainly have returned.

His was one more in the long list of bitter disappointments suffered by early explorers. He had been sent to find the Columbia and instead had come upon a river impossible of navigation then or now. Yet it was a notable achievement. One of his biographers has said, "There is no other large river on the Pacific Slope so terrible or so dangerous to follow as the Fraser, unless it be that part of the Snake River between Huntington, Oregon, and Lewiston, Idaho, (Hell's Canyon).

Fraser and his men successfully made their way back up the river, starting on July 3 and arriving at Fort George on August 6. Ironically, the spring run-off from the mountain snows had now ended and they had less difficulty than on their downstream passage. Had they started a little later in the spring, they might have made their journey much more easily. Once back safely, they probably did not care. Grateful that the miserable, disappointing effort was over, they went back to fur trading. Who cared about the Columbia? There were furs enough in Canada.

One man cared—Alexander Mackenzie. For him, even more than for Fraser, this trip meant final disappointment. That same year he returned to his native land, married and bought the estate of Avoch in Ross-shire. He and his wife had three children, a daughter and two sons, and lived the lives of Scottish gentry until his death, March 12, 1820.

Fraser himself was not much impressed by what he had done but others have been. As one biographer wrote: "How difficult it is to distinguish small from great actions! Here was a man making fame for all time and the idea of the greatness of his work had not dawned upon him."

He remained a Nor'wester until that company merged with Hudson's Bay in 1821. Then he retired to his boyhood home at St. Andrews, Ontario, married and settled down. He lived forty more years, dying in 1862 at the age of eighty-six. He had been offered knighthood in recognition of his achievement but had not the means to go to England to receive the honor. Besides, stubborn to the end, he thought that as the nearest relative of the famous Lord Lovat he should have been made Baron Lovat. A mere "Sir" was not enough to tempt him.

Had he known it, a greater honor was given him when his name was bestowed upon the wild, stubborn river he had tamed by mistake.

THE FOURTH ROAD

David Thompson, 1810–1811

I

WHEN Simon Fraser's Indian guides reported to him, that summer of 1808, that another white man had been seen on a river some distance to the east, the person of whom they spoke was Fraser's fellow Nor'wester and friend, David Thompson. Though Thompson himself did not know it, he was at the moment paddling up the Columbia River but in this portion of its twelve-hundred-mile length, it flowed north. For that reason, he thought it must be some other stream. Equally mistaken, though in the opposite direction, was Fraser, who was convinced that he himself was on the Columbia. The two men were very different. Fraser was a born fur trader. It was the life he loved and he asked for no other. Thompson, like Alexander Mackenzie, engaged in fur trading not as an end in itself but as the means whereby he could follow his own purpose. In personality and background, no two could have differed more: Mackenzie, the proud young aristocrat; Thompson, the child of the very poor. He is perhaps the most appealing of all the early explorers, if only because he made so much out of so little.

No picture of him has ever been found but people who knew him said he closely resembled John Bunyan, author of *Pilgrim's Progress*. A friend described him thus:

A singular-looking person, plainly dressed, quiet and observant. His figure, short and compact; black hair worn long all around and cut square, as if by one stroke of the shears, just above his eyebrows. His complexion, ruddy brown; the expression of his deeply furrowed features, friendly and intelligent. His cut-short nose gave him an odd look. His speech betrayed the Welshman. He has a powerful mind and a singular faculty of picture-making. He can create a wilderness and people it with howling savages or climb the Rocky Mountains with you in a snowstorm so clearly and palpably that only shut your eyes and you hear the crack of a rifle or feel the snowflakes on your cheeks as he talks.

This man who so deeply impressed those who knew him had what we today would call an underprivileged childhood. He was born in London, of Welsh parents, April 30, 1770, only two days short of the one-hundredth anniversary of the Hudson's Bay Company, which was to play an important part in his life.

His father died when David was only two and John, his brother, less than two months old. Somehow their mother struggled through the next few years but when David was seven, she led him to the door of the old Grey Coat Charity School for Boys near Westminster Abbey.

"David, I can do nothing more for you. Here you will have a chance for an education. Make the most of it and be a good boy."

"Yes, Mother."

However deep must have been the despair in the little boy's heart, he had long before this learned to accept without protest or question whatever happened. He never wrote of his feelings when the door closed behind his mother's retreating form and he was left alone. So far as we know, he never saw her again but many years later, his brother did visit him once in Canada.

The Grey Coat School, already a hundred years old, was a royal foundation to educate poor boys "in the principles of piety and virtue and thereby lay a foundation for a sober and Christian life." In David Thompson, this purpose was eminently realized.

At this time, England was at war with her former colonies in North America and needed men for her Royal Navy. The Grey Coat boys were taught mathematical and nautical subjects to the exclusion of everything else except penmanship and spelling. Their books were ragged volumes, some as old as the school, but David made the most of every crumb of knowledge they contained.

He was specially attracted toward astronomy and in the summer evenings, when the other boys would be playing, he might be seen standing in the open, gazing up at the stars. His only other recreations were walking through the streets of London and reading the inscriptions on the tombstones in the great abbey.

By the time he was ready to leave the school, at fourteen, the war was over and the Navy was cutting down, rather than adding to, its numbers. What to do with a charity boy who knew nothing except navigation and astronomy? A life saver for the governors of the school was a request from the Hudson's Bay Company in Canada for four apprentices, to serve seven-year terms.

David and one other boy were signed on but at the prospect of crossing the stormy Atlantic, the other lad ran away. Once more, David entered a new life all alone. The little fleet of three Hudson's Bay ships started in June. One went to Moose Factory, one to York Factory and the third, David's ship, to Churchill Factory at the mouth of Churchill River, arriving in September, 1784.

The Factory, a word used to designate the posts where furs were collected and processed for shipment, was a dreary collection of small, hastily built log huts. The Arctic winter had already set in and the cold was intense but on this bleak tundra, fuel was so scanty that the men could have fires only to cook the morning and evening meals. The rest of the day they worked in their beaver coats to keep from freezing. Frost, four inches thick, coated ceilings and walls and kept showering the shivering men with frozen particles. Finally, someone thought of pouring water on it to turn the frost to ice and thus gain a chilly sort of insulation. Spring and summer were not much better. As David wrote in his journal:

> After passing a long, gloomy and most severe winter, it will naturally be thought with what delight we enjoy the spring and summer. Of the former we know nothing but melting of the snow and the ice becoming dangerous; summer, such as it is, comes at once and with it myriads of tormenting mosquitoes; the air is thick with them and there is no cessation day or night of suffering from them.

David wrote a good, clear hand but feared he might lose the ability without practice. He begged copying to do, but the post was short on writing paper, as on everything else. He did have a few books to read, the property of company officers, and from them learned something of natural history.

During the short days, he spent much of his time outdoors, learning to hunt and trap and becoming a crack shot. This ability came in handy the next September when he was sent on foot a hundred and fifty miles to York Factory and had to procure his own food on the way. An amazing test of courage and stamina for a fifteen-year-old boy who never before had lived outside a large city.

Another lonely year and he was moved again, this time hundreds of miles west to the Saskatchewan River, where he helped build a trading post named rather grandly, Manchester House. Here he learned the routine of the fur trade and the scale of prices, with the beaver skin as the unit. It was here, also, that he saw the evil effects of liquor upon Indians, and made up his mind never to use it in trade.

Once, some years later, when his superiors insisted he take along two kegs of whiskey, he obediently lashed them to the sides of a pack horse but made sure it was the wildest animal he owned. Furiously the horse rubbed against trees until he had smashed the kegs to pieces. This action shows one of Thompson's most noticeable traits: never to meet obstacles head on but find a way around them.

While at Manchester House, David broke a leg and had a bad time of it through the winter. When the ice left the Saskatchewan, his friends took him down to Cumberland House which was more comfortable. There, he wrote, "By the mercy of God, the accident turned out to be the best thing that ever happened to me."

This was because Philip Turnor, the Hudson's Bay astronomer, was there and during David's convalescence, taught him to survey, use nautical instruments, take observations of the sun, moon and stars and determine latitude, longitude, time and the variations of the compass. The exactness and precision of these skills suited the temperament of the quiet, methodical youth. Before he had recovered the full use of his leg, he knew this was to be his work in the world.

Maps of Canada were few and poor. In all of them was a great, empty space whose dimensions, even, were unknown, stretching from Hudson's Bay to the Pacific Ocean. This empty space David determined to measure and fill with correctly placed

rivers, lakes, and mountains. To do this would require intermin-
able travel by foot and canoe, with constant observations and
careful notes. For this purpose, the fur trade was excellent.

From this moment on, David Thompson never wavered in
his ambition. Before he finished his work in the Northwest, he
had covered more than fifty thousand miles on foot, horseback
or by canoe, and had filled in that great empty map with data so
precise that later observations have changed them very little.

This great accomplishment was still only a dream, however,
during that winter of his youth when his broken leg was slowly
healing. He devised a set of symbols as a kind of shorthand, to
keep his meteorological notes in as small space as possible. From
this code, many years later, he was able to reconstruct his maps.

Through Philip Turnor he learned what instruments he would
need and ordered them from London. They were few and simple:
two telescopes, one large and one small, sextant, artificial mercury
horizon, watch and compass. These he used throughout his life-
time.

From comments of other traders we learn how impressed they
were with Thompson's simple, sincere religious beliefs and
practices. Every night, even on the trail, he read his Bible by
the light of the camp fire, sometimes to himself but more often,
in very poor French, to the canoemen who traveled with him.

He did not drink or gamble, facts which made him unusual
if not unique among that wild, hard-drinking, hard-living breed
of men. The frequent pious comments in his journal—"By the
mercy of Providence," "For which thank God," "May God bless
our efforts," and the like, were not there by accident but were
the sincere expression of his constant dependence on the Almighty.

Not only did he believe his religion, but he practiced it in
every aspect of his life, even to the use of his time. His working

hours belonged to the company but he considered the night hours his own. While his men slept, he often studied the heavens, marked the passage of the planets, the phases of the moon and the majestic wheeling of the stars about the pole.

The Indians, who loved any kind of ceremony, were much impressed when Thompson made his celestial observations, which must have seemed to them like incantations to a Great Spirit of the Sky. For this, they named him Koo-Koo-Sint, the Man-Who-Watches-Stars.

From the first, Thompson got along well with Indians. He thought of them as no different from other people. Of the Piegans, among whom he spent considerable time, he wrote:

> The character of all these people appears to be brave, steady and deliberate . . . Almost any character in civilized society can be traced among them from the gravity of a judge to a merry jester and from open-hearted generosity to the avaricious miser.

For months on end, he lived with Indians, ate the same food and shared the same tepees. Never having known ease or luxury himself, he was not repelled by their primitive arrangements and habits as were Mackenzie and Meriwether Lewis. He felt sincerely that in being a trader, he was helping them, as he reveals in his notes:

> See the wife of an Indian sewing their leather clothing with only a pointed, brittle bone or a sharp thorn. See the time and trouble it takes. Show them an awl or a strong needle and they will gladly give the finest wolf or beaver skin they have to purchase it.

Or regarding the benefits of flint and steel:

> When the tents remove, a steady, careful old man or

two of them, are entrusted with the fire, which is carried in a rough wooden bowl with earth in it and carefully fed to the place of the camp. A fire is then made and as the tents are pitched and ready, one from each comes for some fire. A flint and steel saves all this anxiety and trouble.

Thompson was not above learning from Indians. One of his friends, old Chief Sarkamappee, gave him this advice:

If one of our people offers you his left hand, give him your left hand, for the right hand is no mark of friendship. This hand wields the spear, draws the bow and the trigger of the gun; it is the hand of death. The left hand is next to the heart and speaks truth and friendship, it holds the shield of protection and is the hand of life.

David Thompson might have gone on all his life as a Hudson's Bay trader and never have been known to the world, but for the surliness of one man, Joseph Colen, Resident Chief of York Factory, where David took his furs and obtained his supplies. He had finished his apprenticeship in 1791 and had served two three-year terms as a trader in the "muskrat country" west of Hudson's Bay, a vast tumble of lakes, streams and marshes, thick with fallen trees and beaver dams. When it came time to sign another three-year contract, Colen said, "You must understand, Thompson, that we've had enough of this star-gazing of yours. If we take you on again, you must swear to spend all your time in trading."

"I never use the time of the company for my observations," Thompson said in his mild, deliberate way. "The time is taken from my own sleep."

"So you aren't as fit the next day," Colen growled. "Make

up your mind. If you want to continue with Hudson's Bay, stop your sky-watching."

How hard it was for a man almost twenty-eight years old to break with the life of ordered discipline he had known from the age of seven, one can only imagine. Never before had he been required to make a major decision. Always there had been someone to tell him, "Go here," or "Do that," and he had done it, faithfully and well. Give it all up for the unknown fortunes of the wilderness?

That night David Thompson must have stayed awake a long time. In the darkness and silence of the wilds the stars burned big and bright as lamps. They had become the one permanence in his life. They told him where he was and where he wanted to go. They had made him a man. His astronomy was his own, the only thing in all his life that he had chosen for himself. His decision was inevitable.

Silently, so as not to waken anyone, he made a pack of his few belongings—a blanket, a tin cup, extra moccasins, a new leather shirt—rolled them around his precious instruments, tied his watch by a leather thong about his neck and thrust his compass, wrapped in deerskin, inside his shirt where his wide belt would hold it against his lean stomach. He strapped his pack to his back, took up his gun and shot pouch and set out into the night.

Some days later, he arrived at Grand Portage six hundred miles to the south, and asked for a job as surveyor and astronomer, with the North West Company, until now his rival. The Nor'westers happened to need a surveyor right then to mark the line between Canada and the United States in the Great Lakes area. They gave him the job and he wrote in his journal:

May 21, 1797. This day left the service of Hudson's Bay Company and entered that of the Company of

Merchants from Canada. May God Almighty prosper
me.

2

FOR the first time in his life, David Thompson now had an assign-
ment at the work he loved and for a whole year did not have to
trade furs to earn his living. In high spirits, he set off south from
Grand Portage in the fall with seven French Canadian voyageurs,
a guide, interpreter and one trader. He and the guide rode horseback, the rest of the party on dog sleds, since the snow already
was deep. The temperature dropped to forty-one degrees below
zero, with blizzards that blotted out all landmarks. Only by
means of Thompson's compass were they able, on December
30, to reach the Mandan Villages where they remained until
spring.

Their job was to survey and map what are now the northern
portions of North Dakota, Minnesota and Wisconsin and determine the source of the Mississippi River. The forty-ninth parallel had been set as the tentative border between Canada and
the United States. Thompson surveyed this parallel and placed
markers, then went all the way around Lake Superior. In ten
months he surveyed more than four thousand square miles of
territory, more than anyone else had accomplished in ten years.

Among the effects of his work was the necessary removal
of the North West Company's headquarters from Grand Portage,
shown to be below the border, to a new site, Fort William, at
the mouth of the Kamenistiqua River. This operation cost the
company ten thousand pounds.

In June, 1799, when he was twenty-nine years old, Thompson
married Charlotte Small, fourteen-year-old daughter of Patrick
Small, a trader of Irish and Scottish ancestry, and a Chippewa

woman. It seems odd to readers of his journal that Thompson almost never mentions his family, though his habit of taking them with him on most of his travels proves his devotion. The Thompsons ultimately had seven sons and six daughters, most of whom grew to maturity.

For several years, Thompson traded along the Saskatchewan and Athabasca rivers, making his headquarters at Rocky Mountain House. Every spring he took his winter gathering of furs the long journey to Fort William, exchanged them for trade goods and returned in time to begin trading again in the fall. This routine was broken by that one trip with Duncan McGillivray to try to cross the Rocky Mountains. Left by McGillivray the next spring with an order to continue his search for the Columbia, Thompson seems to have felt no particular urgency in carrying it out. To do so would mean fighting the Piegans and he had no relish or forces for such an undertaking. Better to wait his chance for a peaceful crossing of the pass. So the years went by and the Columbia remained unexplored.

Then, six years after the McGillivray fiasco, Thompson's opportunity came. This was not through a change of heart on the part of the Piegans, but through another of those strange interplays between expeditions.

It will be remembered that in the summer of 1806, when Lewis and Clark were returning from the Pacific, Lewis and a few of his men had made a side trip up the Marias River where they were jumped by a band of Indians. In the resulting skirmish, two tribesmen were killed but the white men got back safely to their comrades on the Missouri. For Lewis, this ended the affair.

Not so the Indians. The two victims were relatives of the Piegans and Blackfeet. Their deaths must be avenged. Con-

sequently, in 1807, the whole Blackfoot nation left its usual
summer haunts to patrol the Missouri River, far to the south.
Any white man who had ventured up that stream that summer
would automatically have met death. Apparently none did.

Because of this avenging action, however, the Piegans had
left unguarded the pass at the head of the Saskatchewan. David
Thompson, waiting patiently near by, saw his chance and slipped
through the narrow defile, a mere crack in the tremendous range
of the Canadian Rockies, with snow-capped peaks ten thousand
feet high and higher all about him. Today we know this area
as Banff National Park.

As usual, he had with him his family, consisting of his wife
and three small children, as well as a party of men equipped to
establish a trading post on the western side of the range.

Their route brought them to the head of Blaeberry Creek
which is not, as Thompson then thought, the head of the
Columbia River but does empty into it. Here, under date of
June 27, 1807, he wrote:

> We came to a little rill whose current descends to the
> Pacific Ocean. May God in his mercy give me to see
> where its waters flow into the ocean and return in
> safety.

His joy was short-lived. Only five days later, when he reached
the large stream he had expected would be (and actually was)
the Columbia, he found it flowing north. He must be mistaken.
So much for that. He had made it over the pass and now must
go on with his job of fur trading, by which he made his living.
Facing him, across the beautiful valley where the pines and firs
stood thick as fur on the hills, rose in the background the snow-
white peaks of another mountain range, of whose existence he

had until now been ignorant. He named the range the Nelson, in honor of Lord Nelson who had just won the battle of Trafalgar. Later, Governor George Simpson of Canada wished to honor his own friend, Lord Selkirk, and gave the range the name it bears today.

Curious to see where this river took its rise, and believing he would find beaver country to the south, Thompson went upstream until he did come to the source of this lovely north-flowing river in a small lake now called Columbia Lake. Years later, after he had learned the true names of both, he wrote:

> Other rivers have their sources so ramified in rills and brooks that it is not easy to determine the parent stream; this is not the case with the Columbia River. Near the foot of a steep, secondary mountain, surrounded by a fine grassy plain, lies its source in a fine lake of about eleven square miles of area, from which issues its wild, rapid stream, yet navigable to the sea.

In this summer of 1807, not knowing its identity, he named it the Kootenay, from an Indian tribe of the vicinity. A few miles downstream he built his trading post, Kootenay House, and there spent the next winter. It was not a peaceful year. When the Piegans came back from their fruitless vigil on the Missouri and learned that in their absence Thompson had gone over the pass, they swarmed furiously about his little stockade. It took all his powers of persuasion, plus his friendship with certain important chiefs, to avert bloodshed.

When spring came, he packed up the furs he had secured, left a few men in charge of the post and hastened back the way he had come, to Rocky Mountain House on the Saskatchewan, where he left his family. Down the long course of this mighty river and over the "carries" he made the tedious circuits, knowing

it would be four months before he could be back at his post,
ready to trade for another winter.

Historians have wondered why he did not send one of his
men on this wearisome journey while he used the summer to
continue searching for the Columbia River. That he did not
is proof he had not been made to feel that the task was vital
and urgent. He also had a personal reason for taking the trip.
He confided this reason to his journal:

> To ascertain the height of the Rocky Mountains above
> the level of the ocean had long occupied my attention
> but without any satisfaction to myself. I had written to
> the late Hon. William McGillivray to buy for me a
> mountain barometer for the measurement of these
> mountains. He procured one which he placed in the
> hands of Mr. John McDonald of Garth, a Partner,
> with a promise to take great care of it and deliver it to
> me in good order, but he tossed it on the loaded canoes,
> where it was tossed about and when he brought it to
> me at the foot of the mountains the case was full of
> water and the barometer broken to pieces.
>
> Mr. William McGillivray bought for me another ba-
> rometer which unfortunately was delivered to the same
> person, who made the same promises, with the same
> performance; seeing it was hopeless to procure a baro-
> meter, I had to follow the best methods of measure-
> ment which circumstances allowed. By a close estimate
> of the descent of the Columbia River from its source to
> the sea, I found it to be 5,960 feet in 1,348 miles,
> being an average of four feet, five inches per mile . . .
> The base line here was carefully measured and the an-
> gles of the heights taken with the sextant in an arti-

ficial horizon of quicksilver. By this method I found the height of Mt. Nelson to be 13,123 feet above the Pacific Ocean. (Actually, it is 12,125 feet.)

Knowing his passion for surveying, we can understand from his frustrations about the barometer, why he made that long trip in both 1808 and 1809, hoping to receive intact this instrument he so much needed.

Before he started East in the spring of 1809, Thompson again pushed a little farther into the wilderness. Indians had told him that only a mile on beyond Columbia Lake there was another big river which did flow south. Perhaps this might be the Columbia.

Hopefully, he crossed the flat strip of land, later called Canal Flats when a steamboat canal was cut across from one river to the other. Here, sure enough, he found the south-flowing stream, a wild, beautiful river to which has since been transferred the name Kootenay, spelled Kootenai where it crosses into the United States. The mystery deepened. Was this the true Columbia or did the other one somehow double on itself farther to the north?

Thompson had not the geographical intuition of Captain William Clark. All he had was his careful, hard-won knowledge of surveying, plus great physical stamina, patience and the "infinite capacity for taking pains," which has been called the basis of true genius. Willing to wait for Nature to reveal herself, he paddled down the Kootenay in the beautiful month of April, with wild flowers blooming at the edge of the receding snow line and pines and firs sending up their tender green "candles" on every branch. On May 6 he arrived at a camp of Kootenai and Flathead Indians near the present town of Bonners Ferry, Idaho.

He could not stay long to explore again; he must take the winter's catch of furs to Rainy Lake in time for the annual shipment to Fort William and Montreal, but he did promise the Flatheads to come back in the fall with a supply of trade goods.

He did not forget his promise. That November he sent his assistant, big, redheaded Finan McDonald and a half-breed, Jacques or Jocko Finlay, down the Kootenay. Near today's site of Libby, Montana, the two men put up a temporary log warehouse, later moving it to a more permanent post near Jennings, Montana. The same year, they built still another, Saleesh House, on the Clark Fork River, not far from Woodlin, Montana, and Thompson traveled all through northern Idaho and a corner of Washington, slowly unraveling the tangled skein of the Clark Fork, Pend Oreille and Kootenai rivers, but leaving unexplored, the Columbia. Once, on the Pend Oreille, he was only a few miles from its confluence with the Columbia when the falls of Box Canyon barred his way. True to his nature, he turned aside and went another way. Had he felt the push of Meriwether Lewis when stopped by the Great Falls of the Missouri, he would have gotten around them and discovered his south-flowing Columbia two years earlier than he eventually did.

Still once more, in the spring of 1810, he made the long trip to Rainy Lake, where some of the partners held a conference to discuss what the Americans were up to now. For some time the Nor'westers had been hearing of Col. John Jacob Astor's plan for establishing trading posts across the United States, with a supply base at the mouth of the Columbia—Mackenzie's old plan brought up to date.

Possibly at this meeting Thompson received orders to hasten down the Columbia to the mouth before the Astor party could get there. His journal makes no mention of such an order but for some reason he had come to the decision that this was the time. The next summer, he would descend the Columbia to the sea.

3

Again, Thompson's purpose was to be thwarted. Upon his return to Rocky Mountain House to prepare for his usual trip across Mountain Pass, he found the Piegans once more up in arms. He knew them well enough not to try to force the issue but he still did not give up his plans. Instead, he determined to find another pass one hundred and twenty-five miles farther north on the Athabasca River beyond Piegan territory, where he would not be bothered in subsequent trips.

Though it was late in the fall, Thompson left his family in the comfort of Rocky Mountain House and started out with twenty-four picked men whom he called "the bravest and hardiest of a hundred hardy men." They left on October 28, with twenty-four horses, each carrying one hundred and eighty to two hundred and forty pounds of supplies. Four men were employed as hunters, two to clear a path through the woods, one Indian, Thomas, as guide and the rest to tend the horses.

Forest fires had raged through the area, leaving so many burned and fallen trees their progress was cut to eight miles a day. Horses had trouble squeezing through the trees with their loads. Everyone was soaked and chilled, there being no warmth in deerskin clothing when wet.

After a month of misery, they came to the Athabasca River and began ascending it toward the mountains. Here the snow was so deep they could no longer use horses and had to send all but four of the strongest ones back to Rocky Mountain House. They camped for a few weeks to prepare snowshoes and sleds, and to build log huts for storing the goods and provisions they could not carry farther. The temperature went down to thirty-two degrees below zero and the men crowded into the little huts to stay alive.

On December 30, they started over the mountains with dog sleds. Each sled pulled by two dogs carried one hundred and twenty pounds; one-dog sleds had seventy pounds. The four horses were loaded with meat, pemmican, grease and flour. On up the Athabasca, sometimes traveling on ice and sometimes plowing through the woods. When they came to a place free of snow, blowing sand was just as bad. The second day they had to reduce the weight on the sleds by one-third and cache the extra supplies in a log "hoard."

Thompson noticed that while his men built the log hut, they twice took time to cook and devour a four-gallon kettle of meat, though they had had a hearty breakfast. Never too patient with the voyageur, he vented his annoyance in his journal that night:

A French Canadian has the appetite of a wolf and glories in it; each man requires eight pounds of meat per day or more. Upon my reproaching some of them with their gluttony the reply I got was, "What pleasure have we in life but eating?"

A French Canadian, if left to himself and living on what his Master has, will rise very early, make a hearty meal, smoke his pipe and lie down to sleep and he will do little else through the day. To enumerate the large animals that have been killed and I may say devoured by my men would not be credible to a man of regular life, yet these same hardy Canadians, as years have proved to me, could live upon as little as any other person. In their own houses in Canada a few ounces of pork, with plenty of coarse bread and potatoes, are sufficient for the day and they are content.

New Year's Day, 1811, came in with minus twenty-two degree weather but a big feast. The hunters had been fortunate in killing two young bulls and a mountain sheep. The men marched all day until after four o'clock, then camped on beds of pine boughs in the shelter of the trees. One of the habits of the Canadians which most distressed Thompson, though he could not always prevent it, was the way they flogged their dogs, sometimes to death. This had happened to several animals so the number of sleds had to be cut to eight, with two dogs to each and the horses to assist as far as the depth of the snow would permit. Again they cached the extra goods they could not carry.

They were now entering the rugged defiles of the mountains, where the stunted pine trees, aspens and willows were full of branches clear to the ground, making movement through them almost impossible.

The only grass available for the horses dwindled to narrow strips around marshes and ponds. They were forced to leave the poor, tired creatures here with no shelter, not daring to hope they would live, as it proved they did, until the next spring.

Warm winds from the Pacific began to melt the snow and the thermometer rose to twenty-two degrees. Thompson knew they must be close to the divide. The country was wild and desolate, all wind-swept cliffs and towering, snow-covered peaks, among them some of the highest of the Canadian Rockies. Wood was so scarce they had to camp most of the night without fire. Ahead, loomed a glacier of a clear green color, two thousand feet high. Despite their fear and nervousness, the men admired the brilliance of the stars at this height. One said he could almost touch them with his hand.

The next morning, after a bit of exploring, Thompson concluded they had passed the divide and were on the west side
of the mountains. When he returned to camp, he found the men
boring into the snow with twenty-foot poles to find how deep
it was. He told them that while they had good snowshoes, it was
no matter whether the snow was ten or a hundred feet deep.
On looking into the hole they had bored, he noticed that the
color of the sides was a beautiful blue; near the surface very
light, but darker as it went down and at the bottom, almost
black.

> Many reflections came on my mind. A new world was
> in a manner before me and my object was to be at the
> Pacific Ocean before the month of August. How were
> we to find provisions and how many men would remain
> with me, for they were dispirited. Amidst various
> thoughts, I fell asleep on my bed of snow.

Going down the mountains brought them into a very different
climate and among huge cedar, fir and spruce trees, often ten
to fifteen feet in diameter, standing so thick they shut out the
sun and turned day into night. Often the trail was so steep the
dogs could not guide the sleds and wrapped themselves around
the trees, dogs on one side and sled on the other.

Once down to more level country, they set up a camp and
Thompson sent part of the men back for the goods they had had
to leave behind. Some of them kept on going and never did show
up again. Eventually the party reached the Canoe River and
followed it down to the Columbia. Here, Thompson found the
solution of the mystery. The Columbia, at this point, makes the
first of its big bends and turns south. How long Thompson had
suspected this fact, he never mentioned, but here it was, proved
at last, by his careful foot-power method.

Here, at a camp he named Boat Encampment, where the fur brigades of later years changed from canoes to horses and vice versa, Thompson set about building a canoe in which to go to the sea. There was no birch "rind" even "thick enough to make a dish," he wrote, so they had to use thin boards of cedar, six inches wide, which they split from some of the huge trees which so dismayed the men. These they "sewed" to the ribs with the fine roots of pine trees. By mid-April, they had finished a canoe twenty-five feet long and Thompson was ready to take off down the Columbia on his ten-year-delayed voyage to the sea.

Again, he was thwarted in his plans. Of the "twenty-four brave, hardy men," only three remained who were willing to go on with him, too weak a party to travel among strange and perhaps hostile Indians. He would have to go to his trading posts on the Kootenai and Clark Fork, where he might find men sufficiently courageous. So up the Columbia he paddled, filling in one gap in his travels, the ninety miles between Canoe River and his first camp at the mouth of Blaeberry Creek. On May 9, the party "had the pleasure of camping on ground clear of snow," though the mountains still glistened in the spring sunshine as white as in winter.

Five days later, they reached Canal Flats or, as it was then called, McGillivray's Crossing, portaged to the Kootenay and paddled on down to visit the trading posts. These included the new Spokane House recently set up by Finan McDonald and Jocko Finlay on the east bank of the Spokane River, nine miles downstream from the present city of Spokane.

In mid-June, he made a three-day horseback trip across country to Kettle Falls, on the Columbia, and there spent two weeks building another canoe. Kettle Falls, where the river dashed over a precipice into huge cauldron-like holes, was a famous fishing place of the Indians, now deep under the waters of Roosevelt Lake, behind Grand Coulee Dam.

Here Thompson encountered the same legends regarding the salmon as Mackenzie had met among the Bella Coolas. The beach must be kept very clean and no part of the salmon, after it was brought on shore, ever put back into the river.

The fish must be scaled and cleaned some distance back from the water and care taken not to disturb the river in any way. Even a dog, lapping up a drink, would send the salmon off down the current. The Indians fished with spears, but if a salmon were loose on the spear and got away, fishing must end for that day.

By dint of much persuasion, Thompson now had secured eleven men to accompany him to the sea, including two San Poil Indians for interpreters.

> After praying the Almighty to protect and prosper us on our voyage to the ocean, early on the third of July, we embarked.

A day or so later, he wrote:

> We set off on a voyage down the Columbia River to explore this river in order to open out a passage for the interior trade with the Pacific Ocean.

Again, the fur trader speaking, with no thought about securing the country for Great Britain. His earlier comment in his journal that he must be at the ocean by the first of August may well have been made because he thought that date the latest time which would permit a return to his posts by winter.

Now that the trip had actually begun, it was to prove quick and easy. The stream was running high and rapids and falls offered less trouble than at other times of the years. The first day, they passed the mouth of the Spokane River and reached the San Poil. Here they sent an invitation to the chiefs of the village to come and smoke.

Two San Poils took turns telling the news of their country. At the end of every three or four sentences, they stopped and the chief repeated the same in a very loud voice so all could hear. He was answered by a strong "Oy, Oy."

After this briefing session, the women and children were allowed to come and make a present to the white man of roots and berries. As the pipe went around, each man was allowed three hearty puffs while the women were permitted only one. Thompson noticed that each woman made her puff a long one.

He explained that he was going to find out the conditions of travel to the sea. If they proved good, large canoes with goods of all kinds would soon arrive. This news seemed to please the Indians and the evening ended with dancing.

On July 9, Thompson and his party reached the confluence of the Columbia and the Snake, then called the Shawpatin, and camped near the place where Lewis and Clark had stopped six years earlier. Here he set up his famous pole and wrapped around it a notice written on a thrifty half-sheet of paper:

> Know hereby that this country is claimed by Great Britain as part of its territories and that the North West Company of Merchants from Canada, finding the factory for this people inconvenient for them, do hereby intend to erect a factory in this place for the commerce of the country around.
>
> D. Thompson
>
> Junction of the Shawpatin River with the Columbia, July 9, 1811

A few miles below the Snake, Thompson met Chief Yellepit of the Walla Walla tribe, a tall, handsome, six-footer about forty years old. He was clean and well-dressed, intelligent and friendly.

> He made no speeches, but talked man to man, and told us of their helpless state unless the white man would bring them arms, ammunition, axes, knives and many other things.

> We informed him that we had armed all the natives, particularly the Saleesh and Kootenais, and that as soon as possible we should do the same to his people. That the way we brought the goods at present obliged us to cross high mountains and through hostile people; that we now sought a short, safe way, by which all the articles they wanted would come in safety.

Like all the explorers who came this way, Thompson commented on the poor living conditions of these river Indians and especially on their lack of natural mechanical skills. They had no weapons of war, rarely even bow and arrows; not a single stone axe and only sharp stones for knives with no handles.

> An Eskimo with their means would soon have stone tools and kettles to hold water and boil their fish and meat; whereas all these tribes do not appear to have anything better than a weak small basket of rushes for this purpose.

Other traits were equally baffling:

> We hardly knew what to make of these people; they appeared a mixture of kindness and treachery; willingly rendering every service required and performing well what they undertook but demanding exorbitant prices

for their services and dagger in hand ready to enforce their demands . . . They steal all they can lay their hands on and nothing can be got from them which they have stolen.

In its physical aspects, this was a discouraging place to live. Then, as now, the great bare hills and bluffs presented an awesome grandeur but little vegetation to sustain man or beast. They were swept by strong, hot winds and scoured by blowing sand. No trees, except now and then a dwarfed fir. For fuel, driftwood from the river.

Worse than this, to Thompson's men, were the poisonous black rattlesnakes that infested the river banks.

On going ashore, our custom always was to throw part of our paddles on the grassy ground and although we think we can see everything on the short, scanty grass, yet by doing so we are almost sure to start one of these snakes that we did not see. Every morning we rose very early, while the dew was falling, and tied up our bedding as hard as we could. These were two blankets or one with a bison robe, and when we put up for the night did not untie them until we lay down, by which time they were all withdrawn into their holes in the sands, for they always avoid dew and rain and they are fond of getting on anything soft and warm.

One evening, seeing a convenient place and a little wood, we put up rather early and one of the men undid his blankets and laid down. The fish was soon boiled and we called him to supper. He sat up but did not dare to move. A rattlesnake had crept in his blanket and was now half erect, within six inches of his face, threatening to bite him. He looked the very image of

despair. We were utterly at a loss how to relieve him
but seeing several of us approaching, the snake set off
and left us.

Before long, the beautiful white cone of Mt. Hood loomed
in the distance and the men saw Indians fishing with nets and
using canoes made of trees that had drifted down the stream,
one thirty-six feet long. This was near the mouth of John Day
River and here Thompson first heard that an American ship
had arrived at the mouth of the river, Astor's *Tonquin*.

If he was disturbed by the news, Thompson made no record
of it. He was absorbed in the difficulties of the river. Near The
Dalles, it ran between high perpendicular walls of basalt which
contracted it into a sixty-yard channel.

> Imagination can hardly form an idea of the working of
> this immense body of water under such compression,
> raging and hissing as if alive.

The men had to carry everything, including the canoe, around
this terrific rapids, but once below:

> Trees are once more in sight, a most agreeable change
> from the bare banks and monotonous plains. Snow
> covered mountains lie ahead.

Another day and they came to the series of rapids called the
Cascades, now deep in the lake behind Bonneville dam. Another
portage, and soon they approached their journey's end.

> According to custom, the men put on their banners and
> ribbons and hoisted the Union Jack to leave no un-
> certainty as to the country represented.

Gabriel Franchère, who was then living at Astor's post,
describes the arrival of the Thompson party:

> Toward midday we saw a large canoe with a flag displayed at her stern, rounding the point which we called Tongue Point . . . A well-dressed man who appeared to be the commander was the first to leap ashore.

As Thompson tells it:

> On the 15th near noon we arrived at Tongue Point, which at right angles stretches its steep, rocky shores across the river for a full half mile, and brought us to a full view of the Pacific Ocean; which to me was a great pleasure, but my men seemed disappointed. They had been accustomed to the boundless horizon of the great lakes of Canada and their rolling waves. From the ocean they expected a more boundless view, a something beyond the power of their senses which they could not describe. And my informing them that directly opposite to us, at the distance of 5,000 miles, was the Empire of Japan, added nothing to their ideas, but a map would.

Thompson thought he was looking at the ocean, but he was still two miles from Astoria, a huddle of low log huts, and seven miles from the open sea. The spread of Young's Inlet and the ten-mile width of the Columbia at this point deceived him.

In charge at Astoria, Thompson found two men he knew, Duncan McDougall and David Stuart, former clerks of the North West Company. They greeted him warmly and made him and his party welcome. One wrote:

> Mr. Thompson kept a regular journal and traveled, I thought, more like a geographer than a fur trader.

Perhaps, as some have thought, McDougall and Stuart, though

in Astor's employ, still thought of themselves as Britishers. Certainly, between them and Thompson, there was no animosity in spite of the rivalry between their companies. He thought poorly of their post:

> The quality of their goods is very low but good enough for the beggarly natives around them. These appeared a race of worthless, idle, impudent knaves, without anything to barter, yet begging everything they saw.

Thompson has now almost completed the task he set himself years before:

> Next day in my canoe with my men, I went to Cape Disappointment, which terminates the course of this river, and remained until the tide came in. Thus I have fully completed the survey of this part of North America from sea to sea, and by almost innumerable astronomical observations have determined the positions of the mountains, lakes and rivers, and other remarkable places in the northern part of this continent.

On his way back, he left the Columbia at "the forks," ascended the Snake to the mouth of the Palouse River, then went overland to Spokane House, thence to Kettle Falls, his starting point. Here he made another canoe and returned to Boat Encampment by way of the Arrow Lakes, the part of the river he had never before seen. He thus became the first man to travel the entire length of the Columbia.

A few more years of trading and he went back over Athabasca Pass for the last time. He was forty-two years old, his children should be in school, and he wanted to complete his life work by drawing an actual map on which his observations were made visible. He spent the years 1813 and 1814 preparing this great map, five feet by eight in size, using a scale of fifteen miles to the inch. When finished, he turned it over to the North West Company and for years it hung on the walls of the dining hall at Fort William. Other map makers used it with no credit to Thompson. In his modest, self-abasing way, he made no complaint.

For ten years, from 1816 to 1826, the government employed him to survey the boundary line between Canada and the United States and he became quite wealthy for those days. Then, through his own generosity, he lost his life savings. A church to which he had loaned ten thousand dollars could not pay, so Thompson, true to his nature, deeded to it the church building and grounds. His sons failed in business and he paid their debts though it took everything he had.

At seventy, he went back to surveying but before long his eyesight failed. He wrote up his notes into his famous *Narrative,* and hoped to sell it. Washington Irving heard of it and tried to buy it but, according to one of Thompson's daughters, failed to offer enough money or to satisfy Thompson about acknowledgement of authorship. There were no other bidders and the narrative, like the map, remained unpublished until Dr. Joseph B. Tyrell, a member of the Geological Survey of Canada, stumbled onto them in the 1880's and brought them to public notice.

Thompson died in poverty on February 10, 1857, at the age of eighty-seven. His faithful wife outlived him only three months and both lie in unknown, unmarked graves. Not until many years later did people become interested in this shy, modest genius but from that time to the present, his stature has steadily increased until now he stands as one of the greatest, if not the greatest, of all the early explorers.

THE FIFTH ROAD

The Astorians, 1811–1812

I

THE same year, 1784, that Alexander Mackenzie left Montreal for Detroit with his first stock of trade goods, another young man, exactly his age, arrived in New York City, also bent on making his fortune in furs. He was John Jacob Astor. The lives of the two were to be intertwined in important ways though they came from very different backgrounds and approached the fur business with different motives.

Mackenzie, following the custom of the North West Company, had begun at the bottom, had undergone five years of stringent apprenticeship and still was on a lower rung of the ladder leading to a partnership.

Astor, with no training at all, was about to begin at the top, as an independent trader; no partner, but owner, proprietor and sole beneficiary of his business.

Yet, where Mackenzie failed, Astor succeeded. Mackenzie had to see his great patriotic dream hamstrung by the commercial ambitions of his partners. Astor, with no dreams of national sovereignty mixed into his equally commercial ambitions, still planted the Stars and Stripes where and when it would do the most good.

Even more noteworthy is the fact that Mackenzie wrote the book which inspired Astor's great plan, another example of the inter-relationship of the expeditions. Too often overlooked in accounts of the early explorers is the influence of certain books: Jonathan Carver's *Travels,* which fired the imagination of Alexander Mackenzie; Mackenzie's own *Voyages,* which helped activate the Lewis and Clark expedition; the *Journal* of Patrick Gass, which spurred the North West Company into sending Fraser and Thompson across the Rockies; and the effect of both Mackenzie's and Gass' books on John Jacob Astor.

Astor had no desire to become an explorer; that was the farthest thing from his intention. He was forty-eight years old when he dispatched the expeditions that bear his name, and then he did not go himself as did the others whose names head the great explorations. He formed the plan and furnished the money, a most important contribution, but he sent others to do the actual exploring.

His story begins in the small German village of Waldorf, in the Duchy of Baden, where he was born July 17, 1763. His father, a butcher, expected his three sons, George, Henry and John Jacob, to come into the shop with him. In this he was disappointed. George went off to London and opened a music store, Henry took his butcher trade to New York and Jacob, at seventeen, decided he would not be the only one left behind.

Already he felt a certainty that some day he would be wealthy though he could not yet see how it could happen. He had no special skill and no remarkable education. Alone, on foot, he set out for the River Rhine. On the way, resting under a tree, he took stock of himself. Three things he resolved—to be honest, to be industrious and not to gamble. The first two he followed consistently but the third—perhaps any investment of large sums of money is something of a gamble and, as the years went by,

Astor invested a great deal. But back to the boy sitting under the tree.

A job on a raft taking timbers down the Rhine provided passage money to London. There he worked in his brother's music store for three years, saving his money and learning English, though he never could speak it without an accent. In appearance, he was a stout, squarely built youth, five feet nine inches tall and destined to become portly as he grew older.

Everyone in London was talking about the new nation, the United States, then still at war with Great Britain. As soon as the peace treaty was signed, Jacob took passage for America in the steerage of a sailing ship, where he had nothing to eat but salt beef and biscuits. He had twenty-five dollars in cash and a small stock of musical instruments, including seven flutes, with which to make his fortune.

The ship entered Chesapeake Bay early in January, 1784, but was frozen in for two months before it could reach port. During this time, Astor became acquainted with another young German who had made the trip before. He was engaged in buying and selling furs and painted the future of that business in such bright terms that before Jacob ever stepped ashore, he had mentally discarded music for furs.

This German friend, John N. Emerick, later claimed half of Jacob's fortune on the grounds of having supplied the original inspiration, but at this time all was pleasant between them.

Astor's capital still tied up in the seven flutes, he went to New York, as his new friend advised, and there set up a tiny shop in Water Street, said to have been the first store in America exclusively for the sale of musical instruments. There being no buying rush, Jacob had to turn to other work for a while. Then he persuaded his brother Henry to take charge of the store while he began traveling up the Mohawk Valley, trading cooking utensils and trinkets for pelts. Indians brought him their small catches and he found farmers who did some trapping on the side. In a few months he had accumulated a respectable pack of furs and sailed off to London where he disposed of them at a good profit. He also picked up information from dealers how to go about this business.

Three years after he arrived in New York, Astor married Miss Sarah Todd, daughter of the widow with whom he boarded. His bride, in addition to a keen intellect and good sense of fur values, brought him a dowry of three hundred dollars cash. This was a large sum in those days and gave the young couple a fine start in their business.

When Astor learned that Montreal was the fur capital of North America, he began going there to buy furs, shipping directly to London himself. He also persuaded a merchant friend to take a cargo of furs to China. Astor's own profit from this first venture is said to have been fifty thousand dollars. He seemed to have the Midas touch. By the end of the century, his fortune amounted to a quarter million dollars, not only from the fur business but from his extensive dealings in Manhattan real estate.

Perhaps it was on one of his Montreal trips that he acquired a copy of Mackenzie's new book, *Voyages,* and read the explorer's plan for supplying inland trading posts from a base on the Pacific Coast. At once, Astor saw its possibilities and adopted it for his own, waiting only for the right time to put it into action.

After Thomas Jefferson was elected President and sent Lewis and Clark to explore the West, Astor watched with eagerness for reports of the trip. The *Journal* of Patrick Gass, published only a few months after the successful return of the expedition, gave him the information he needed. Mackenzie's dream could be transplanted to American soil. A string of trading posts up the

Missouri and down the Columbia, supplied from a center at the mouth; furs from inland posts collected at this base, shipped to China and there exchanged for tea, silks and porcelains so much desired in England and America—what could be more beautifully logical?

As his dream expanded, he added a second line of trading establishments down the Mississippi with another base at St. Louis, whence furs could be shipped up the Ohio to New York. Even that was not enough. There were Russian ports on the Pacific Coast that could be served as part of the routine trip to the Orient. Nothing less than world-wide trade could satisfy the ambition of John Jacob Astor.

Looked at from the present, the plan has a twentieth-century flair, worthy of today's global vision of commerce.

Astor began action on his plan with the organization of the American Fur Company, chartered by the state of New York to trade in the upper Mississippi Valley. This area was dominated by Canadian traders, a condition he proposed to change. He offered a share in it to the North West Company if they would merge with him. One can almost hear the explosion that greeted this proposal. "That American upstart? Who does he think he is?"

Astor took the snub and waited his time. When the Mississippi division was going well, he began the western development. For this he organized twin expeditions, one, a ship loaded with supplies, to go around the Horn and up the Pacific Coast to the mouth of the Columbia; the other overland following the route of Lewis and Clark. As this one progressed across the country, it was to establish trading posts along the way. When the two groups met, the company would be in business.

To operate this specific part of his enterprises, Astor created the Pacific Fur Company, a subsidiary of his overall American Fur. The date was June 29, 1810. The firm was capitalized at two hundred thousand dollars, divided into one hundred shares. He retained fifty for himself, assigning the rest to his partners and clerks in varying amounts. He was to provide all equipment, ships, provisions, arms, ammunition, trade goods, etc., and bear all losses for five years, up to four hundred thousand dollars. The partners were to put in their knowledge and skill. It was a fine, generous plan, depending only upon the ability of the men who administered it.

Here Astor's usual good luck deserted him, his choice of leaders being unfortunate. For his principal partner, head of the overland expedition and administrator on the West Coast, he named Wilson Price Hunt, a native of Hopewell, N. J., who had moved to St. Louis a few years before and there had become a successful merchant.

What induced Astor to think Hunt capable of the job or Hunt himself to undertake it, has never been explained. He was twenty-eight years old and above reproach in character but there his qualifications ended. Never in his life had he commanded men, let alone the rough, independent sort who would go on such an expedition. He had never traveled through unknown country and knew absolutely nothing of wilderness life.

This mistaken choice was partially offset in the beginning by the fact that Hunt's assistant and co-leader was a former Nor'-wester, Donald McKenzie. This young man was a brother of Roderick and cousin of Alexander Mackenzie, though he chose to spell the family name differently. He had come out to Canada as a youngster, been apprenticed to the North West Company like his brother, and at this time had worked for them ten years. He was, therefore, well versed in wilderness life and proven as a fur trader. A huge man, well over six feet tall and weighing more than three hundred pounds, he was still agile and athletic. Most Indians thought twice before challenging him. Whatever Hunt lacked in experience, McKenzie could have supplied if permitted to do so. Perhaps this was Astor's reasoning. Had he left well enough alone, it might have worked.

Through his visits to Montreal, Astor had acquired great respect for North West men and now, with offers of partnerships and shares in the profits, he lured four more of them away from his competitors. They were: Duncan McDougall, an experienced though, as it proved, undependable trader; Alexander McKay, who had accompanied Mackenzie on both his expeditions; David Stuart and his nephew, Robert Stuart, the youngest of the group.

McDougall was to take charge of the sea expedition and be Hunt's second in the administration on the West Coast. This was almost as poor a choice as that of Hunt. McDougall had been a wilderness man all his days. He knew the ways of Indians and canoemen but the confinement of a ship drove him mad. Some historians have found reason to believe that he joined as an undercover agent for the North West Company. This has never been proved but later actions indicate something less than loyalty to Astor. Not only was McDougall a Britisher. The same was true of all the other partners except Hunt, eight of the eleven clerks and fifteen subordinate employees who went by ship.

These last were Canadian voyageurs who had been employed in Montreal. Eight of them, led by Alexander McKay, chose to make the trip to New York by canoe. Down the Richelieu and the length of Lake Champlain they paddled, singing at the top of their voices:

> "A frigate went a-sailing,
> *Mon joli coeur de rose,*
> Far o'er the seas away,
> *Joli coeur d'un rosier*
> *Joli coeur d'un rosier,*
> *Mon joli coeur de rose*"

Then down the Hudson, banners flying, plumes waving, and gallant young men in fringed deerskin shirts flirting with every country maid they saw. Word ran along the farmers' grapevine to New York and a breathless messenger rushed into Astor's office.

"Mr. Astor! Mr. Astor! They are coming!"

Out to his dock stalked the portly financier, in his formal clothes of black broadcloth and high beaver hat. Proudly he watched the beautiful, slender birchbark canoe glide down the choppy East River. New Yorkers had never seen such a sight as this and a crowd lined the water front, so thick the panting reporters sent on the run by their editors could hardly squeeze through.

Up to the dock swept the frail craft and out jumped the eight stalwart Canadians, following their leader who held out his hand to his employer.

"Here we are, Mr. Astor."

"Velcome to New York."

At a signal from McKay, two of the men lifted the canoe from the water to their shoulders and marched toward a shed where it could be put under cover. Mr. Astor saw the amazement in every eye as the boat which had held all nine men was thus lifted by only two. His men! In delight, he beckoned to McKay and pressed a gold double eagle into his hand. "See that they have food. And perhaps, a drink to my health."

Astor had reason to be proud not only of his crew, but also of the ship he had bought for the expedition. She was the *Tonquin,* a stout little vessel of two hundred and ninety tons with ten guns and a crew of twenty. For master, he engaged Lt. Jonathan Thorn, an officer in the U.S. Navy, on leave of absence.

Thorn seems to have been upright, honest and intelligent but so accustomed to commanding sailors who jumped when he spoke that he could not accept the role of captain of a passenger ship. He insisted on extreme details of military discipline from all the civilians aboard, even the partners. They, in turn, were not about to become dutiful underlings and let him know it. Trouble began even before the ship left New York harbor.

Of all this, Astor was happily unaware on the September day in 1810 when he stood with his wife on the dock as the *Tonquin* sailed bravely down the bay. His great undertaking was at last under way. He waved his beaver hat and Mrs. Astor raised her carefully gloved hand in salute. Then they went home to dinner.

Jacob was proud of himself. The poor German lad was at last coming into his own. A few more years, a few supply ships sent to the West Coast, and people would see. He would be emperor-in-fact over the entire North American fur trade. Most of it done with North West men, too. That company would be sorry it had refused to join him.

"You don't think, Papa, that anything bad can happen to that fine ship and those nice young men?" Mrs. Astor asked wistfully.

"Now, Mamma, vot could happen? It is a good ship and Thorn is a good captain. Things happen to careless men but I am not careless. Everything has been planned. You vill see. All vill come right."

"But so long to wait before we hear," sighed Mamma.

So very long, if only Jacob had known it and then, what terrible news!

2

As the *Tonquin* sailed down the bay, she was joined by the frigate *Constitution*, sent as an escort to protect her from British war vessels known to be hovering near for the purpose of impressing American seamen. This was one of the situations which led to the War of 1812, now rapidly approaching though Astor did not seem aware of it or of the danger that might threaten his new establishment on the Pacific.

From the first day aboard, there was trouble between the captain and his thirty-three passengers. In assigning places on the ship, he sent the mechanics forward among the common sailors. They had been employed as future clerks and expected berths suitable to this station. Thorn rigidly denied their claim and threatened to "blow out the brains of the first man who dares disobey my orders on my own ship." Only the diplomacy of David Stuart, "a good old soul," as one clerk called him, prevented an out-and-out fight.

As the ship's escort left her, and she went on down the coast of South America, the men were bored with inactivity. One day they devised a game of target-shooting, suspending a mark from the ship's stern, under which a small boat lay secured. Some time afterward, as darkness was coming on, someone saw smoke and the alarm of fire was sounded. Sailors and passengers reacted as human beings of today often do. According to one account:

> In an instant, all the people assembled on deck in a state of wild confusion, some calling out to broach the water casks, others running to and fro in search of water, some with mugs, others with decanters, while the cook was robbed of his broth and dishwater; no one, in the hurry and bustle of the moment, ever thought of dipping the buckets alongside.

Presently the fire was discovered to be in some canvas that had been left in the small boat and set on fire by gun wadding from that target practice. It was quickly put out and the sport forbidden.

As winter approached, the ship encountered fierce gales that lasted forty and fifty hours, forced leaks in the seams, blew the sails to rags and dismounted six of the guns, which kept rolling dangerously about the deck.

Stopping briefly at one of the Falkland Islands, near the tip of South America, a few of the men went ashore and one inadvertently lay down, falling asleep in the warm sunshine. When sailing time came, he did not appear. After much urging, the captain agreed to wait one hour only. If the man did not show up, they would sail away and leave him.

Several of his friends volunteered to search for him. Some set fire to a few tufts of grass, hoping he would see the signal. Finally, the man woke up, unaware of the trouble he had caused. Before the party could reach the ship, the hour had elapsed. The loss of a few more minutes so enraged the captain that he "not only threatened the man's life but maltreated all those who had been instrumental in finding him."

Not long after, when the ship was anchored near shore for a few days while the water casks were replenished and necessary repairs made, the captain became angered and set sail without nine of the Canadians, including McDougall and David Stuart. Having seen how ruthless and headstrong he could be, they knew he would not come back or wait for them. If they reached the ship, it must be by their own efforts. Alexander Ross, one of the clerks in the party, tells of the bitter experience:

> We had to stow, squat and squeeze ourselves into a trumpery little boat scarcely capable of holding half our number. In this dreadful dilemma we launched on a rough and tempestuous sea and against wind and tide followed the ship. The wind blowing still fresher and fresher, every succeeding wave threatened our immediate destruction. Our boat already half full of water,

and ourselves, as may be supposed, drenched with the surges passing over her, we gave up all hope of succeeding in the unequal struggle, and a momentary pause ensued, when we deliberated whether we should proceed in the perilous attempt or return to land.

The ship was now at least two leagues ahead of us, and just at this time the man who was bailing out the water in the boat unfortunately let go and lost the pail, and one of our oars being broken in the struggle to recover it, our destiny seemed sealed beyond a doubt . . . The sun had just sunk under the horizon and night began to spread its darkness . . . Every ray of hope now vanished; but so shortsighted is man, that the moment he least expects it, relief often comes from an unseen hand, and such was our case.

They saw the ship coming about and in a short time were alongside. Here they were in great danger of being dashed to pieces by the heavy seas when they tried to board her but eventually they succeeded after more than six hours in the small boat. They learned that the captain had intended leaving them to their fate and would have done so except for young Robert Stuart who,

seizing a brace of pistols, peremptorily told the captain to order about the ship and save the boat; or, he added, "You are a dead man this instant."

Compared to this episode, the former squabbling between captain and passengers seemed insignificant.

Sullen and silent, both parties passed and repassed each other in their promenades on deck without uttering a word; but their looks bespoke the hatred that burned within.

The partners now thought up the device of talking only in the Scottish dialect while the Canadians on the forecastle spoke in French. Since the captain understood neither, he was kept in a state of suspicious ignorance.

Amid all this bickering and even hatred, the good little ship continued to plow along, and on Christmas morning, doubled the Cape and started north, preceded by a little pilot fish of whom the men became quite fond. It stayed with them until they crossed the equator and all felt the loss of a pet when it left.

On February 13 the *Tonquin* anchored in Kealakekua Bay on the Island of Hawaii. Here some of the outraged sailors deserted. Those the captain could find and bring back, he treated unmercifully:

> Storming and stamping on deck, the captain called up all hands; he swore, he threatened and abused the whole ship's company . . . I really pitied the poor man, although he had brought all this trouble upon himself.

Generously, the partners, clerks and Canadian boatmen helped out. After a pleasant stay in Hawaii, which included a state call on King Kamehameha, the party once more set sail on March 1, 1811, for the Columbia River. The departure was made miserable by Thorn's threat to leave behind any man who was an instant late for the shore boat. One man was actually deserted here and others flogged within an inch of their lives, yet so strong was Thorn's discipline that nobody interfered.

Toward the middle of the month the weather turned very cold, with snow and sleet. The partners wanted to give out some articles of clothing to the shivering passengers but the captain refused to let a single box or bale be opened. Pistols came out again, until once more the oldest partner aboard, David Stuart, prevented violence. The captain kept his bales and boxes untouched and "the men froze in the icy rigging of the ship until many of them were obliged to take to their hammocks."

Despite gales and freezing weather, on March 22, the ship came in sight of Cape Disappointment, the promontory on the north side of the Columbia at the mouth. She stood off about ten miles until the captain made sure this was the entrance of the river. He then ordered Mr. Fox, the first mate, to take a small boat and look for the channel.

Fox objected to trying it in such weather and such a rough sea, adding that the waves were too high for any boat to live.

"Mr. Fox," said Captain Thorn, "If you are afraid of water, you should have remained in Boston."

At this, Mr. Fox ordered the boat to be lowered. It was small and not seaworthy; the crew composed of the four poorest sailors on the ship. The partners remonstrated with the captain over the folly of sending them out until the weather should change. With his usual stubbornness, anything they said only made Thorn more furious and Mr. Fox was ordered to proceed.

> He, seeing that the captain was immovable, turned to the partners with tears in his eyes and said: "My uncle was drowned here not many years ago and now I am going to lay my bones with his." He then shook hands with all around him and bade them adieu. "Farewell, my friends! We will perhaps meet again in the next world."

The words were prophetic. Before the little boat was a hundred yards from the ship, she capsized and soon sank with all aboard.

The next day, some of the partners and clerks, skippered by Mr. Mumford, the second mate, made several attempts to find the channel but the waves and surf drove them back. Being displeased with Mr. Mumford, the captain then sent the third mate, Mr. Aikens, with four men, to sound in a more northerly direction and if he found three and a half fathoms of water, to hoist a flag for a signal. At three in the afternoon of March 25, the pinnace hoisted the flag and the ship stood in for the channel.

> At the same time the boat, pulling back from the bar, met the ship about half a mile from the breakers, in eight fathoms, going in with a gentle sea breeze, at the rate of three knots an hour.

The small boat steered a little to one side to be out of the ship's way and, to the horror of all on board, the captain passed her without speaking a word or stopping to take the men on board. Frantically, the partners called for a rope to be thrown overboard to save the men but the captain replied, "No, I will not endanger the ship."

So four more good men went to their deaths in the surf while the ship herself struggled among reefs and shoals all night. Toward morning, the incoming tide lifted her off the rocks and carried her safely into Baker's Bay.

Next day, some of the angry passengers wandered the beach, hoping the small boats or some of the men might have survived. They found one man alive, and one dead body but of the others, no trace ever appeared.

Now came the important task of choosing a site for the trading post. Following the experience of Lewis and Clark, six years earlier, the partners decided the best place was on the south bank. There, under direction of Duncan McDougall, whom Astor had named to head the enterprise until Mr. Hunt's arrival, the men began clearing land for buildings.

McDougall, writes Alexander Ross, was "a man of but ordinary capacity, with an irritable, peevish temper, the most unfit man in the world to head an expedition or command men."

In addition to coping with an irritable leader, the men must try to subdue a forest of huge fir trees, many measuring fifty feet in girth and so close together and so intermingled with great rocks, the task was almost impossible. Some of the same trees still stand today in this area of Oregon. A section of one, at the site of the Astor memorial tower in Astoria, measures ten and one-half feet in diameter and was two hundred and fifty-seven years old when cut. No one in or planning the Astor expedition had anticipated anything like this and no saws had been provided. As Ross describes it:

> Every man, from the highest to the lowest, was armed with an axe in one hand and a gun in the other; the former for attacking the woods, the latter for defense against the savage hordes which were constantly prowling about . . .

> It would have made a cynic smile to see this pioneer corps, composed of traders, shopkeepers, voyageurs and Owyhees (Hawaiians) all ignorant alike in this new walk of life, and most ignorant of all, the leader. Many of the party had never handled an axe before and but few of them knew how to use a gun, but necessity, the mother of invention, soon taught us both.

The trees were so large, the men built rough scaffolds about them on which to work, and with nothing but axes, took as long as two days to chop through one of the immense trunks. No one knew how to tell where a tree would fall, so spent much time in guessing and in jumping out of the way.

> The trees would still stand erect, bidding defiance to our efforts, while every now and then some of the most impatient or foolhardy would venture to jump on the scaffold and give a blow or two more. Much time was spent in this desultory manner before the mighty tree gave way, but it seldom came to the ground. So thick was the forest and so close the trees together, that in its fall it would often rest its ponderous top on some other friendly tree.

In two months of incessant toil, the men had cleared less than an acre of ground but during this time, three had been killed by Indians, two wounded by falling trees and one had his hand blown off by gunpowder. Worse than the work was the climate. Damp fog and sleet were constant companions and it rained every other day. The men had no tents or shelter, the food was bad, no salt was available and half the party were sick.

McDougall, comfortable in his quarters aboard ship, and well fed from her stores, paid little attention to the sufferings of the men. It now became apparent how mistaken Mr. Astor had been in sending no doctor and in placing so unsuitable a man in charge. The only hopeful thing in the place was the sight of the little green shoots in the potato patch the men had set out the moment they landed.

The unequal struggle with the giant fir trees at length brought a halt to the plan to clear land and use these great trees in their building. The men went back in the forest for smaller trees, then, having no animals to haul them, harnessed themselves together, eight to a team, and dragged in enough logs for a store building sixty by twenty-six feet in size. On May 18, when the first foundation was finished, the post was christened Astoria in honor of the founder.

Captain Thorn, who had been waiting impatiently for the trade goods to be removed from his ship, unloaded as much as could be stored though only a small part of the supplies, intending to put the rest on shore when he came back from the trading trip he was itching to take. With him, as supercargo, or business representative of the owner, went Alexander McKay. His authority was supreme in matters of business, while the captain had authority over the navigation of the ship. As his assistants, McKay took one clerk and two Canadians.

Before his departure, McKay married a daughter of the one-eyed Indian chief, Comcomly, who thereupon acquired great status among the Indians. He also was well aware that the little post was helpless if his people chose to be hostile. Though he was a braggart and a nuisance, he still was the sole protector the Americans had and he did not allow them to forget it, swaggering around in a red coat and plumed hat, demanding daily gifts.

It was while matters stood in this rather hopeless state that David Thompson appeared, dashing down the river in his light canoe manned by eight men. "McDougall received him like a brother," reports Ross, hinting that in his estimation the two were maneuvering even then for the British to take over the post.

Meanwhile, the *Tonquin* had reached the vicinity of Vancouver Island and dropped anchor in a bay where the natives were known to be hostile. In doing this, Thorn, as usual, disregarded all advice and stubbornly demonstrated who was boss of the ship. Not only was he indifferent to plain common sense, but he disobeyed Astor's specific commands by mistreating the Indians, insulting the chiefs and allowing a horde of savages to come on board his ship.

Suddenly, out from under the blankets came the knives and tomahawks. When the slaughter was over, Thorn, McKay and the clerk were dead, with all the sailors except five, who barricaded themselves in the cabin. Next day one white man went on deck and beckoned the Indians to come on board. When the ship was crowded with loot-happy savages, the powder magazine exploded, carrying to destruction everything and everyone on board, except three men who were later caught and killed, and one Indian interpreter, who escaped. Months later, this lone survivor made his way to Astoria with the tragic story, but it would be another year before John Jacob Astor, busily loading a supply ship for the post, would get the news.

3

We must now go back almost a year to July of 1810, when Wilson Price Hunt and Donald McKenzie set out for Montreal to sign up a party for the overland expedition. McKenzie shared Astor's preference for Canadian voyageurs, with whom he had worked for ten years, over American men who were apt to be too independent. He announced his desire to employ all the men they would need right here in Montreal.

Hunt was not so sure. "These Canadians, they are like children," he grumbled. "They say they will join up, they accept the advance money I give them and then—poof, they are gone."

"They are afraid," McKenzie said.

"Of what?"

"Of leaving their own country and going to the ocean. And they do not want to sign up for five years."

"I think the North West Company is trying to discourage them from going with us. They don't like Mr. Astor."

"Why should they?" McKenzie laughed.

"Anyhow, I've wasted enough money here on men who run

away the moment they have spent what I gave them. Let's go to Michilimackinac. There must be men there who will be willing to go with us."

"Things will be worse there than here," McKenzie protested, but Hunt would not listen. To Mackinac they went.

This place, located at the juncture of Lakes Michigan and Huron, was headquarters for the Mackinaw Company, a smaller but still powerful British trading firm. Here, as McKenzie had prophesied, it was as hard to find men as in Montreal, if not harder. Once more, Hunt paid out considerable sums in advance, only to find that the men had vanished without qualms.

"I don't know what to do," he confessed.

"I have an idea," said McKenzie. He bought a supply of ostrich feathers and plumes and began giving them to the men who remained loyal to Hunt, as a sort of uniform. The vain, rather childish voyageurs strutted about the post, showing off their finery and bragging of the coming expedition. Soon men were flocking to Hunt's party.

At this point, the leader had one real stroke of good luck, when he engaged Ramsay Crooks, an experienced trader and trapper, destined in years to come, to be one of the leaders of Canada.

He now had secured thirty men, which he thought enough, but Crooks insisted he needed twice that number to journey safely through Blackfoot and Sioux country. Hunt, who preferred Americans anyhow, decided to wait until he reached St. Louis to find the rest.

So early in August, down to St. Louis they went, via Green Bay, the Fox and Wisconsin rivers to Prairie du Chien, and the Mississippi. Here Hunt encountered another rival, the Missouri Fur Company, represented by Manuel Lisa, a capable and experienced trader. From the first, Lisa tried to be friendly to Hunt, though freely acknowledging the fact that they were in competition. Hunt, however, was suspicious and decided to move his men up the Missouri to the prairie country. Here they could hunt for their own meat, and in addition, be removed from Lisa's influence. By November 16, having employed thirty more men, Hunt took his crew north as far as the Nodaway River and made camp for the winter.

Shortly thereafter, a messenger reached him with dispatches from Astor. Not content to leave arrangements as they had been settled in New York, or perhaps responding to complaints from Hunt, Astor demoted McKenzie to a subordinate position, giving Hunt sole command of the expedition. This widened a rift already opened between the two and denied to Hunt the benefit of McKenzie's experience, which he sorely needed. He made things worse by promoting to partnership one Joseph Miller, a former army officer who had joined the party, and he himself returned to St. Louis for more men and supplies. Miller and McKenzie did not get on well together and all winter the feud continued.

In St. Louis, Hunt's chief business was to hire an interpreter and after considerable looking about he chose Pierre Dorion, a Sioux halfbreed. Dorion had been with Manuel Lisa, who naturally resented Hunt's luring him away. Suspicion between the two increased steadily, though from the distance of today, Lisa seems to have behaved very well. He even proposed that the two parties join forces in their journey up the Missouri, for mutual safety. Hunt would have none of this.

Back up the river he went, his numbers now increased to the sixty men Crooks had insisted he needed, plus Dorion, his Indian wife and two children. He arrived at camp on April 17 and, as soon as the spring rains ceased, the cavalcade started. They passed the mouth of the Platte on April 28, the Omaha villages, May 10 to 15, and arrived at the Aricara villages, July

18. This was the place where trouble with the Sioux was likely to begin.

Manuel Lisa, whose expedition had been moving rapidly from St. Louis, caught up with Hunt at this point and heard, to his surprise, that Hunt had decided to follow Lewis and Clark's route no farther. Listening to the Indian guides, he had been frightened into believing that his well-armed party of sixty could not get through Blackfoot and Sioux country. Therefore, he had decided to leave the river and journey overland to the Rocky Mountains. In vain did Lisa try to convince him he would be in worse trouble this way; he would not listen.

The fear evidenced by the leader conveyed itself to the men. Wild tales circulated through the camp. Ahead were strange, terrible beasts, dragons, giants and fierce pigmy warriors. The Rocky Mountains were higher than the Himalayas, with peaks soaring twenty-five thousand feet into the sky. They would all die in the miserable cold.

Seeing that Hunt was determined to carry out his decision, Lisa did what he could to help by buying Hunt's boats and paying for them with horses which he would need for the overland journey.

The party set out: sixty-one men, one woman, two children and eighty-two horses. They rode cautiously, with scouts ahead and on both flanks; at night, camp guards and horse guards. At the very end of the column rode the Indian woman with her four-year-old son behind her and the two-year-old in her arms. She proved to be one of the bravest of the party. Humble and uncomplaining, even at her husband's frequent beatings, she won the respect and liking of the men, despite the fact that an Indian woman was considered little better than an animal.

Brief diary jottings quoted in Washington Irving's famous book, *Astoria*, indicate the route followed:

Aug. 14, Little Missouri
Black Hills in view.
On divide, between the Missouri and Yellowstone
Bighorn Mountains
Sept. 9, Wind River
Sept. 15, Sighted Tetons
Crossed the main divide to the Spanish River, a headwater
of the Colorado
Away to the northwest again

Here Hunt once more refused to take advice of trappers who knew the country and turned south, from Wind River. Unbelievably, he did get over a pass and, on October 8, reached Henry's Fort, a primitive log bastion built a year or so before by a trader named Henry, on what is now Henry's Fork of the Snake River, in southern Idaho. They found the post abandoned but at least it was shelter of a sort.

All the way along, dissension had been rife, not only among the leaders, but also in the ranks. The Americans disliked and distrusted the Canadians, and vice versa. The Americans, accustomed to horses, wanted to ride clear to the Pacific; the Canadians longed for the swift travel of birch canoes. Miller, the new partner, an erratic, unreliable man, sided with the Canadians and persuaded Hunt to abandon the horses and continue by water. The other partners protested but to no avail. Again, Hunt showed his lack of self-confidence and his inability to lead.

For two weeks, the men did nothing but cut trees and build canoes, fifteen of them. The horses were left in charge of two Snake Indians—the last any white man ever saw of them. Then, gaily, the Canadians led the way in their canoes and for a day or two the troop was in high spirits. This was real traveling.

They came to the confluence of the little Henry's Fork with the Mad River, the combined stream becoming the Snake.

From this point on, even the most optimistic voyageur had to admit the whole idea of water travel was a mistake. Rapids, whirlpools, falls, all contrived to make further canoeing impossible. Again they were on foot in strange, wild country, game scarce and winter coming. The only Indians who remained in the mountains through these months were a few separated, half-starved families who had been unable to go on with the tribes. Snow deepened; food became so scarce that a dog, a skeleton horse or a beaver skin looked like a feast.

Misled as they had been and now in danger of death, these were brave men. Resolutely, they went on. On October 28 the canoe in which Mr. Crooks was trying to explore ahead, was wrecked on a rock and one man drowned. They named the place Caldron Linn or Devil's Scuttle Hole and here they stopped. Even Hunt saw they could go no farther until scouts had made advance explorations. He sent parties along both banks, taking the right one himself. When they came back for consultation, the men who had gone down the left bank thought boats could be used about six miles farther on.

Four canoes were lifted to husky shoulders and carried the six miles, then set in the stream. Two were lost, though the men in them escaped, and they all returned to Hunt, shaking their heads. John Reed, one of the clerks, then took three men and went on foot to explore. The folly of having abandoned the horses became clear to everyone.

Hunt sent Crooks back with five men to try to regain the horses. McLellan, another clerk, took three men and started downstream to reconnoiter. Donald McKenzie, who had a better feeling for geography than Hunt, urged that they go north to the headwaters of the Clearwater, the route taken by Lewis and

Clark out of these same mountains. Hunt would not listen so McKenzie took four men and started on his own. Hunt and the remaining men began digging caches for the goods Astor had intended them to use in trade. As to establishing trading posts, that part of the plan seems to have been lost completely.

After three days, Crooks came back, having discovered that they had come too far by canoe to be able to return to Henry's Fort. Two of Reed's men showed up with the report that the farther they went, the worse the river became. Well they might say so. The Snake flows across southern Idaho in a deep, rocky trench too steep for man or beast to descend or ascend. It twists and turns, stands on edge, whirls in great maelstroms that suck in even huge fallen pines, spewing them out miles downstream, chewed to shreds by hidden rocks. In addition, the course of the stream was broken by enormous falls: Twin Falls, with a drop of two hundred feet and Shoshone Falls, one hundred and eighty feet, with others only slightly less. Certainly, no canoe could live in this river. In later years, covered wagons were to lumber along these cliffs. People would be driven mad looking down at the water far below, cool and green or foaming like sherbet, while men and animals died of thirst because they could not get down to it.

Hunt and his men once more sorted their goods and cut down to the barest necessities that they could carry on their backs. The rest was placed in nine caches. Hunt divided the men into two parties, one for each side of the Snake. He took the right bank with twenty-two men and the Dorion family; Crooks, with eighteen men, took the left. On November 9 they left Caldron Linn on their desperate journey.

For a month the two parties did not see each other though they were moving at about the same slow rate along the Snake. Hunt was able to purchase a few horses to carry the packs and on one,

Madame Dorion and her two little children rode. One day Hunt heard a hail from the other side and there was Crooks, whose men were in even more destitute condition than Hunt's. He begged for food and Hunt agreed to share what he had. Using the skin of a dead horse, he stretched it over bent tree branches to form a canoe and sent over some meat. One of Crooks' men became so frantic at sight of it, he plunged into the water, upset the canoe and was drowned.

At the mouth of the Weiser River, both parties camped while hunters went out in search of deer. Crooks became very ill and one of his men, John Day, brought him across to Hunt for help. Hunt could not hold the entire party here for Crooks to recover, so left him in camp with John Day, whose name remains on a river emptying into the Columbia, and four Canadians who refused to try to cross the Blue Mountains in winter.

On the day before Christmas, Hunt's party crossed to the left bank of the Snake, near where the town of Weiser, Idaho, now stands, and struck off inland, reaching the Grand Ronde valley a week later. During this week, Madame Dorion gave birth to her third child, which survived the cold only a few days. With deep grief, the more poignant because it was silent, the Indian woman saw her baby buried and went on. Like Sacajawea, she was one of the bravest of the whole party.

Over the difficult Blue Mountains at last, the party reached the warm, pleasant Umatilla valley and rested for two weeks among friendly Indians. With the goal of the journey now in sight, Hunt went on north to the Columbia, crossed to the north bank and continued down the river to Long Narrows, now The Dalles. Here he learned that white men had established a fort at the mouth of the river. This was his first assurance that the other half of the Astor expedition had arrived. He learned also that McKenzie and his party, including Reed and McLellan, whom he had found wandering half dead in the mountains, had passed on down the river a month before.

McKenzie, as it turned out, had followed his own true instinct for directions and had reached the Clearwater, by which he descended to the Snake and Columbia as had Lewis and Clark seven years earlier. He arrived at the ocean in mid-January, 1812, a month ahead of Hunt.

After Hunt left, Crooks had soon recovered enough to travel, so he and Day started out to follow Hunt's trail. For a while, the Canadians went with them but in February they deserted for good. The two men thus left alone lost Hunt's trail but did reach the same Grand Ronde valley where they stayed until late in March. They then went on to the Columbia and were kindly received by friendly tribesmen who gave them food and sent them on their way.

Near The Dalles, they were attacked by the thieving bands of Indians occupying this area, that already had begun to prey on travelers, especially those in small, weak parties. They stripped the two men of their clothing and guns, beat them and left them half dead on the river bank. Feebly, the two started back hoping to reach the friendly tribe that had been so good to them.

Suddenly, a miracle happened. Dashing down the river, manned by voyageurs, came a canoe with two more white men in it. The half-dead wanderers shouted and waved their arms until the canoe turned in toward shore. The leader was their friend David Stuart, who had been up the Columbia to open a new post at Okanogan. He took the two strays on to Astoria, arriving there May 1.

At last the party was reunited, except for the four Canadians who had deserted and two small hunting parties that had started out on the Snake River and had never returned—thirteen men in all. Seven of them reached Astoria almost a year later, January 15, 1813.

Hunt could now tally up the results of his efforts. He had left St. Louis March 12, 1811, and arrived in Astoria eleven months later. He estimated he had traveled 3500 miles in three hundred and forty days, of which at least one hundred and forty had been spent in camp or in the back-trailing he had done from time to time. By direct route, it was 2300 miles from St. Louis to Astoria, so he had wandered 1200 miles unnecessarily.

All the partners, except McKay, who had been lost on the *Tonquin,* were now together at Astoria and the post could begin operations. A meeting was convened and assignments made:

David Stuart to go back to Okanogan, explore the country northward and place another post between himself and North Caledonia, Simon Fraser's location.

McKenzie to winter in the Snake country, recover the goods left in caches by Hunt, and continue trading.

Mr. Clarke, a clerk raised to the position of partner, to go up the Spokane River and set up an intermediate post between Stuart on the north and McKenzie on the south.

Robert Stuart to proceed overland to St. Louis with dispatches for Mr. Astor.

Wilson Price Hunt to accompany the supply ship *Beaver,* which arrived at Astoria May 9, 1812, on a trading trip up the coast.

The plan was well conceived but several unfortunate things happened to mar it. The skipper of the *Beaver,* Captain Sowle, was as autocratic as Captain Thorn of the *Tonquin.* After a successful trading trip to the Russian ports in Alaska, he chose to sail directly to the Hawaiian Islands and refused to let Hunt off at Astoria.

While in the islands, Hunt heard rumors of war between

Great Britain and the United States but nothing certain until
the arrival of the ship *Albatross* from Canton, when the rumor
was confirmed. Hunt chartered this ship and sailed for Astoria
where he arrived August 20, 1813, more than a year after he had
left. In the meantime, dire calamities had occurred.

The partners who had gone inland had also heard rumors of
war from some of the North West men who occupied posts—
Spokane House, Kullyspell House and Kootenay House—estab-
lished by David Thompson and now doing business with the
Indians. They told the Americans that a British ship, the *Isaac
Todd*, was on its way to capture Astoria.

Perhaps the natural alarm felt by the Americans was augmented a bit by the British among them, especially McDougall
and McKenzie. Whether or not, since Hunt had not returned by
the time of their annual meeting, and for all they knew might
be dead, they decided they would sell out to the North West
Company one year later unless peace should be concluded by
that time. McDougall was to remain in charge at Astoria until
Hunt returned—if he ever did. The rest of the partners went
back to their posts to trade as much as possible with the *Beaver*
stock of goods during the winter.

This was the situation when Hunt arrived in August. Protest
as he might he could do nothing to break the agreement the other
partners had signed, McDougall having the right to act in his
absence. Hunt himself was compelled to recognize the probability that the fort would sometime be seized by the British so that
a sale was perhaps the best way out of the dilemma. After a week
at the fort, he went off in his chartered ship to try to arrange
purchase of another vessel to carry away the furs which so far
had not been included in the sale.

All the men had by this time accepted the fact of the transfer
to come the next spring and were making the best possible use of

the remaining time for trading when, early in October, down the Columbia came a large party of North-Westers, seventy-five of them, in a fleet of ten canoes. They picked up the Astor men from the interior posts and brought them along, whooping and yelling in their delight that soon they were to meet the *Isaac Todd* and take possession of the American fort. In charge was George McTavish, a relative of the redoubtable Simon.

Their numbers alarmed the Astorians and won over McDougall. The sale agreement, including all the furs, was drawn up without waiting for the next spring as had been earlier agreed. According to Alexander Ross, one of the clerks who was present, the property and furs were sold for about ten per cent of cost and charges, the price being eighty thousand, five hundred dollars.

Washington Irving in *Astoria* assesses the price as about one-third the amount Mr. Astor had invested. The difference may indicate that Ross includes in "cost and charges" the time and labor of the men who had put in almost four years of their lives, besides incredible hardships, and had received almost nothing in return—except fame in later generations, of which they then knew nothing.

Having made the agreement, the North-Westers showed no hurry about signing it. The Americans finally ferreted out the reason. If the British ship came in, it could seize the fort and the property would be turned over to the North West Company with no purchase at all.

Friendly as McDougall was, and a Britisher, this was too much for him. Ross tells how he brought the matter to a decision:

> One morning before daylight, Messrs. McDougall and McKenzie summoned all hands together, seventy-two in number, and after a brief statement of the views of the North Westers in reference to the negotiation, ordered the bastions to be manned, the guns to be

loaded and pointed and the matches lighted. In an
instant every man was at his post and the gates shut.

At eight o'clock a message was sent to McTavish, giving
him two hours but no more, either to sign the bills or
break off the negotiation altogether and remove to some
other quarters. By eleven o'clock the bills were finally
and formally signed and Astoria was delivered up to
the North West Company on the 12th of November,
1813, after nearly a month of suspense between the
drawing and the signing of the bills.

Only seventeen days later, a British ship did appear; not the
Isaac Todd, after all, but the *Raccoon,* Captain Black commanding. He had hoped to have the honor of capturing the fort but
since the Nor'westers had beaten him to it with their purchase,
he put the best possible face on the situation. He took formal
possession of the post and "the whole country" in the name of
the King of England, renaming it "Fort George." Without intending to do so, the good captain by this action assured final
ownership of the fort by the United States, since when peace
was concluded, each government agreed to return to the other
any places seized during the war.

Meanwhile, Mr. Hunt had had no success in his effort to find
a ship. Indeed, further disaster had occurred in the wrecking of
the *Lark,* a second supply ship which Astor had dispatched to the
Columbia. Completely discouraged, Hunt purchased a smaller
ship, the *Pedlar,* in the Hawaiian Islands, gave her command to
the captain of the *Lark* and returned in her to the Columbia.
Here he found everything finished, the furs sold and nothing
left for him to do but go home. He blamed McDougall for his
handling of the affair though Ross insists that under the circum-
stances, he probably did the best he could.

Mr. Hunt called the men together and, in Ross's words:

> He expressed his deep and sincere regret that so much
> talent and zeal had been employed to no purpose and
> thrown to the winds; that we had been the pioneers of
> a more successful and fortunate rival; that the North-
> Westers would now reap the fruits of our industry; and
> the only consolation left us was that every man had
> done his duty and to circumstances over which we had
> no control might chiefly be attributed the failure of our
> undertaking.

As Ross goes on to say, Mr. Hunt was a conscientious and upright man and this bitter disappointment was not the result of any flaw in his intentions or character. After bidding good-bye to the men, he embarked on the *Pedlar* and took his final departure from Fort George.

Even yet, this was not the end of the sorry story. Donald McKenzie, who had charge of one of the interior forts, had sent John Reed and a party of men during the previous summer to reclaim the goods that had been hidden in caches in the Idaho mountains. They had not returned so Ross and a Mr. Keith set out to try to find them. They had gone up the Columbia as far as the Walla Walla River when they met a few Indians and with them, the wife of Pierre Dorion, their interpreter on the westward journey. She told them her pitiful story.

She and her husband had accompanied Reed into the mountains, where they had been overtaken by winter and had built a house, intending to spend the time until spring in trapping. Indians began to harrass them and several men were killed. At length a friendly Indian came running one night to tell Reed that the Dog-ribs, a band of very bad Snake Indians, were on the warpath and intended to wipe out the white men.

Madame Dorion, terribly frightened, took her two children, got on a horse and rode off through the woods to warn her husband who was trapping some distance away. In the darkness and storm she lost her way and was forced to hide for several days. When she did reach the hut where her husband had been living she found him and all his companions murdered. Turning back to the house where Reed and the others had been preparing to defend themselves, she found them also killed, scalped and cut to pieces. She was alone in the mountains with her two small children.

At first she ran away from the place in horror, then the hunger of her children overcame her fear. She remembered the supplies in the cabin. She wrapped the children in her robe, hid the horse in a thicket, stole back to the house of death and got a quantity of dried fish. Returning to her children, she found them almost frozen, as well as starving. In spite of the danger of detection, she built a fire, warmed and fed the children.

For several days she repeated the process until she had gathered all available food in the hut. Then, placing the load on the back of the horse and the children on top of the load, she made her way through deep snow among woods, rocks and rugged paths for nine days.

Unable to travel any farther and having no tool but a knife, she still succeeded in building a small hut of pine branches, long grass and moss and packed snow around it to keep them warm. She then killed the horse and hung the flesh in a tree for winter food. The hide made extra covering for the children. Here she spent fifty-three days alone with them.

Starting out again, after weeks of travel, snow-blind and near starvation, she had come to the camp of the friendly Walla Wallas. Seldom has a more poignant story of sheer courage been told than that of this Indian woman.

Ross, in recapitulating the tragic history of the Pacific Fur Company, otherwise known as the Astorians, lists the physical losses as including two ships, the *Tonquin* and the *Lark,* a large quantity of trade goods and sixty-one men. So ended the concern which, as he says, "was to have annihilated the South Company; rivaled the North West Company; extinguished the Hudson's Bay Company; driven the Russians into the Frozen Ocean; and with the resources of China to have enriched America."

In spite of the failure, the expedition did make one important contribution to history. It established an American base at the mouth of the Columbia ahead of anyone else, thereby adding greatly to the claim of the United States on the territory now occupied by the states of Washington, Oregon, Idaho and Montana, principal drainage basin of that great river. And this by the narrow margin of the four months between the arrival by sea of the *Tonquin* and David Thompson's arrival by river.

Tribute to the efforts of the Astorians is paid in the name of the city, Astoria, Oregon, built on the site of their fort. On Coxcomb Hill, highest point in the city, stands a hundred and twenty-five-foot column, replica of the Vendome column in Paris and the Trajan column in Rome, about whose face runs the pictorial story of the twin expeditions.

After the fiasco of his Pacific Fur Company, John Jacob Astor retired from the West and gave up his dream of a great fur empire. His other enterprises succeeded so well that when he died, his fortune amounted to twenty million dollars. His seven flutes and twenty-five dollars had brought fabulous returns.

Thus is completed the remarkable story of the five great expeditions across the North American continent to the Pacific Ocean. Within the short space of twenty years, these five groups of intrepid explorers discovered and opened the roads for civilization into the vast area stretching from the Arctic Ocean to the

Columbia and Snake rivers and from the Mississippi and Atha-basca across the Rocky Mountains to the sea.

For the individuals involved, the result was, if not death, impaired health, financial loss and, in all except the Lewis and Clark episode, bitter personal disappointment. Yet because of their efforts the westward march of millions was made possible and the thrilling adventure begun by Columbus three hundred years earlier brought to a brilliant conclusion.

It is appropriate, and a measure of belated recognition, that their names are attached to many of the rivers, lakes, waterfalls and mountains they discovered with such labor and pain, remind-ing both Canadians and Americans for all time of the debt we owe them.

Bill closes the book he and Joe have been reading aloud. From the rooftop of their Seattle hotel he gazes across the sparkling blue waters of Puget Sound to the jagged skyline of the Olympic Mountains, then turns to look eastward to the snow-covered cone of Mt. Rainier, rising more than fourteen thousand feet above the level of that same Sound.

"I guess that must be the height of land old Jonathan Carver dreamed about."

"In a way, he was right," says Joe. "You have to stretch it a bit to see the St. Lawrence rising in the Rocky Mountains but con-sidering the rivers that drain into the Great Lakes, you might almost say it's true."

"What must it have been to see the West when it was all new and fresh!" Bill muses. "I sort of wish I had been one of those explorers myself. Nowadays it seems as if true adventure is over."

"That kind, perhaps, but think of the new roads men of our own day are finding out into space. David Thompson would have made a great astronaut, wouldn't he?"

"Say, that's right. And the new roads in medical knowledge. Lewis and Clark's poor Sergeant Floyd could have been saved with penicillin."

Joe grows enthusiastic. "And understanding people different from ourselves. If Astor's Canadians and Americans had been better friends, they might have made a success of that affair."

"Now I feel better," says Bill. "The way the universe keeps on getting bigger and more complicated, I suppose there will always be new roads to find."

"And always people with what it takes to find them."

Bibliography

Original Sources

CARVER, JONATHAN. *Travels Throughout the Interior Parts of North-America in the Years 1766, 1767 and 1768.* London: Printed for the author, sold by J. Walter, 1778.

COX, ROSS. *Adventures on the Columbia River.* New York: J. & J. Harper, 1832.

FRASER, SIMON. *Journal of a Voyage from the Rocky Mountains to the Pacific Coast, 1808.* Edited by L. F. R. Masson, included in *Les Bourgeois de la Compagnie du Nord-Ouest* (see below).

GASS, PATRICK. *Journal of the Voyages and Travels of a Corps of Discovery under the Command of Captain Lewis and Captain Clark.* Pittsburgh: Printed by Zadok Cramer for David M'Keehan, Publisher and Proprietor, 1807. Edited by Elliott Coues, New York: F. P. Harper, 1893.

HENRY, ALEXANDER (the elder). *Travels and Adventures in Canada and the Indian Territories Between the Years 1760 and 1776.* New York: Printed and Published by I. Riley, 1809. Edited by Milo Milton Quaife, Chicago: The Lakeside Press, R. R. Donnelley & Sons Company, 1921.

HENRY, ALEXANDER (the younger) and THOMPSON, DAVID. *Journals, 1799–1814, New Light on the Early History of the Greater Northwest.* Manuscript Journals edited by Elliott Coues. New York: F. P. Harper, 1897.

LEWIS, MERIWETHER and CLARK, WILLIAM. *Journals,* edited by Bernard De Voto. Boston: Houghton, Mifflin, 1953.

———. *Journals,* edited by Reuben Gold Thwaites. New York: Dodd, Mead and Company, 1904–5.

McGILLIVRAY, DUNCAN. *Journal of Duncan McGillivray of the North West Company.* With introduction, notes and appendix by Arthur S. Morton. Toronto: the Macmillan Company of Canada, Ltd., 1929.

MACKENZIE, SIR ALEXANDER. *Voyages from Montreal on the River St. Lawrence Through the Continent of North America to the Frozen and Pacific Oceans in the Years 1789 and 1793.* London: T. Cadell, Jun., and W. Davies, Strand, 1801. Toronto: Radisson Society of Canada, 1927.

ROSS, ALEXANDER. *Adventures of the First Settlers on the Oregon or Columbia River: being a Narrative of the Expedition Fitted Out by John Jacob Astor, to Establish the "Pacific Fur Company"; with an Account of Some Indian Tribes on the Coast of the Pacific.* London: Smith, Elder and Co., 65, Cornhill, 1849. Edited with Historical Introduction and Notes by Milo Milton Quaife. Chicago: The Lakeside Press, R. R. Donnelley & Sons Company, 1923.

———. *The Fur Hunters of the Far West; a Narrative of Adventures in the Oregon and Rocky Mountains.* London: Smith, Elder & Co., 65, Cornhill, 1855. Edited with Historical Introduction and Notes by Milo Milton Quaife. Chicago: The Lakeside Press, R. R. Donnelley & Sons Company, 1924.

SIMPSON, SIR GEORGE. *Journals.* Edited by Frederick Merk. Cambridge: Harvard University Press. London: Humphrey Milford, Oxford University Press, 1931.

THOMPSON, DAVID. *Narrative of Explorations in Western America, 1784–1812.* Edited by J. B. Tyrell. Toronto: The Champlain Society, 1916.

———. *Journals Relating to Montana and Adjacent Regions, 1808–1812.* Edited by M. Catherine White. Missoula, Montana: State University Press, 1950.

WORK, JOHN. *Journal.* Edited by Henry Drummond Dee. Victoria: Banfold, 1945.

———. *Journal.* Edited by William S. Lewis and Paul C. Phillips. Cleveland: The Arthur H. Clark Co., 1923.

Secondary Sources

BRYCE, GEORGE M. A., LLD. *The Remarkable History of the Hudson's Bay Company.* London: Sampson Low, Marston & Co., 1910.

BURPEE, LAWRENCE J. *The Search for the Western Sea.* New York: D. Appleton & Co., 1908.

———. *On the Old Athabaska Trail.* London: Hurst & Blackett, Ltd., 1927.

CHITTENDEN, HIRAM M. *The American Fur Trade of the Far West.* New York: Francis P. Harper, 1902.

CROUSE, NELLIS M., Ph.D. *In Quest of the Western Ocean.* New York: W. Morrow & Co., 1928.

DE VOTO, BERNARD. *The Course of Empire.* Boston: Houghton, Mifflin Co., 1952.

ELLIOTT, T. C. "David Thompson and Beginnings in Idaho," *Quarterly* of the Oregon Historical Society XXI:49–61, June, 1920.

FERRIS, JOEL E. "David Thompson in Washington." Sandpoint, Idaho: David Thompson Sesquicentennial: 35–47. August, 1959.

FLANDRAU, GRACE. *Astor and the Oregon Country.* Pub. by Great Northern Railway N.D.

———. *Koo-koo-sint, The Star Man.* Pub. by Great Northern Railway N.D.

FULLER, GEORGE W. *A History of the Pacific Northwest.* New York: Alfred A. Knopf, 1949.

HEBARD, GRACE RAYMOND. *Sacajawea, Guide of the Lewis and Clark Expedition.* Glendale, California: The Arthur H. Clark Company, 1957.

HOLBROOK, STEWART H. *The Columbia,* Rivers of America Series. New York, Toronto: Rinehart and Co. Inc., 1956.

HOWAY, F. W. *The Search for the Fraser by Sea and Land.* Vancouver, B. C.: Art, Historical and Scientific Association Session, 1907–8; Historical Papers, 1908.

HOY, CALVIN I. *John Jacob Astor, an Unwritten Chapter.* Boston: Meador Pub. Co., 1936.

IRVING, WASHINGTON. *Astoria.* Philadelphia: Carey, Lea & Blanchard, 1836.

JOSEPHY, ALVIN M., JR. *A Man to Match the Mountains. American Heritage* 11:60–63 October, 1950.

JUDSON, KATHARINE BERRY. *Early Days in Old Oregon.* Portland, Ore.: Metropolitan Press, 1935.

LAUT, AGNES C. *Pathfinders of the West.* New York: The Macmillan Company, London: Macmillan & Company Ltd., 1904.

LAVENDER, DAVID. *Land of Giants: The Drive to the Pacific Northwest, 1750–1950,* Mainstream of America Series. New York: Doubleday & Co. Inc., 1958.

MACLENNAN, HUGH. *Rivers of Canada.* New York: Scribner, 1961.

MASSON, L. R. *Les Bourgeois de la Compagnie du Nord-Ouest.* Quebec: A. Coté et cie, 1889–90.

O'CONNOR, HARVEY. *The Astors.* New York: Alfred A. Knopf, 1941.

PHILLIPS, PAUL CHRISLER. *The Fur Trade.* Norman, Okla.: University of Oklahoma Press, 1961.

PORTER, KENNETH WIGGINS. *John Jacob Astor, Business Man.* Cambridge, Mass.: Harvard University Press, 1931.

SMITH, ARTHUR D. HOWDEN. *John Jacob Astor, Landlord of New York.* Philadelphia: Lippincott, 1929.

SPERLIN, O. B. Articles in *Pacific Northwest Quarterly,* VI:3–11; VIII, 102–113.

TOWNE, CHARLES W. *"Her Majesty, Montana": Highlights in the History of a State Fifty Years Old in 1939.* (Series of 52 Radio Broadcasts Presented by Montana Power Co.). Butte: Montana Standard, 1938–39.

WADE, M. S., M.D. *Mackenzie of Canada; the Life and Adventures of Alexander Mackenzie, Discoverer.* Edinburgh: Blackwood, 1927.

WALLACE, W. STEWART. *Documents Relating to the North West Company.* Toronto: The Champlain Society, 1934.

BEAVER, THE MAGAZINE OF THE NORTH. Winnipeg, Hudson's Bay Company.

COLLIER'S ENCYCLOPEDIA. Crowell-Collier Pub. Co., 1962.

DICTIONARY OF AMERICAN BIOGRAPHY. New York: Charles Scribner's Sons, 1928–1958.

ENCYCLOPEDIA AMERICANA. New York, Chicago, Washington, D. C.: Americana Corporation, 1963.

ENCYCLOPAEDIA BRITANNICA. Chicago, London, Toronto, Geneva: William Benton, Pub. 1962.

ENCYCLOPEDIA CANADIANA. Ottawa: The Canadiana Co. Ltd. 1957.

INDEX